## INDIANS

BLACK HAWK, *Cleven*
OSCEOLA, *Clark*
POCAHONTAS, *Seymour*
PONTIAC, *Peckham*
SACAGAWEA, *Seymour*
SEQUOYAH, *Snow*
SITTING BULL, *Stevenson*
SQUANTO, *Stevenson*
TECUMSEH, *Stevenson*

## NAVAL HEROES

DAVID FARRAGUT, *Long*
GEORGE DEWEY, *Long*
JOHN PAUL JONES, *Snow*
MATTHEW CALBRAITH PERRY, *Scharbach*
OLIVER HAZARD PERRY, *Long*
RAPHAEL SEMMES, *Snow*
STEPHEN DECATUR, *Smith*

## NOTED WIVES and MOTHERS

ABIGAIL ADAMS, *Wagoner*
DOLLY MADISON, *Monsell*
ELEANOR ROOSEVELT, *Weil*
JESSIE FREMONT, *Wagoner*
MARTHA WASHINGTON, *Wagoner*
MARY TODD LINCOLN, *Wilkie*
NANCY HANKS, *Stevenson*
RACHEL JACKSON, *Govan*

## SCIENTISTS and INVENTORS

ABNER DOUBLEDAY, *Dunham*
ALBERT EINSTEIN, *Hammontree*
ALECK BELL, *Widdemer*
CYRUS MCCORMICK, *Dobler*
ELI WHITNEY, *Snow*
ELIAS HOWE, *Corcoran*
ELIZABETH BLACKWELL, *Henry*
GAIL BORDEN, *Paradis*
GEORGE CARVER, *Stevenson*
GEORGE EASTMAN, *Henry*
GEORGE PULLMAN, *Myers*
GEORGE WESTINGHOUSE, *Dunham*
HENRY FORD, *Aird and Ruddiman*
JOHN AUDUBON, *Mason*
JOHN BURROUGHS, *Frisbee*
JOHN DEERE, *Bare*
JOHN FITCH, *Stevenson*
LEE DEFOREST, *Dobler*
LUTHER BURBANK, *Burt*
MARIA MITCHELL, *Melin*
ROBERT FULTON, *Henry*
ROBERT GODDARD, *Moore*

SAMUEL MORSE, *Snow*
TOM EDISON, *Guthridge*
WALTER REED, *Higgins*
. . . GHT,

BETSY ROSS, *Weil*
BOOKER T. WASHINGTON, *Stevenson*
CLARA BARTON, *Stevenson*
DAN BEARD, *Mason*
DOROTHEA DIX, *Melin*
FRANCES WILLARD, *Mason*
J. STERLING MORTON, *Moore*
JANE ADDAMS, *Wagoner*
JOHN PETER ZENGER, *Long*
JULIA WARD HOWE, *Wagoner*
JULIETTE LOW, *Higgins*
LILIUOKALANI, *Newman*
LUCRETIA MOTT, *Burnett*
MOLLY PITCHER, *Stevenson*
OLIVER WENDELL HOLMES, JR., *Dunham*
SUSAN ANTHONY, *Monsell*

## SOLDIERS

ANTHONY WAYNE, *Stevenson*
BEDFORD FORREST, *Parks*
DAN MORGAN, *Bryant*
DOUGLAS MACARTHUR, *Long*
ETHAN ALLEN, *Winders*
FRANCIS MARION, *Steele*
GEORGE CUSTER, *Stevenson*
ISRAEL PUTNAM, *Stevenson*
JEB STUART, *Winders*
NATHANAEL GREENE, *Peckham*
ROBERT E. LEE, *Monsell*
SAM HOUSTON, *Stevenson*
TOM JACKSON, *Monsell*
U. S. GRANT, *Stevenson*
WILLIAM HENRY HARRISON, *Peckham*
ZACK TAYLOR, *Wilkie*

## STATESMEN

ABE LINCOLN, *Stevenson*
ANDY JACKSON, *Stevenson*
DAN WEBSTER, *Smith*
FRANKLIN ROOSEVELT, *Weil*
HENRY CLAY, *Monsell*
HERBERT HOOVER, *Comfort*
JAMES MONROE, *Widdemer*
JEFF DAVIS, *de Grummond and Delaune*
JOHN F. KENNEDY, *Frisbee*
JOHN MARSHALL, *Monsell*
TEDDY ROOSEVELT, *Parks*
WOODROW WILSON, *Monsell*

# F. W. Woolworth

*Five and Ten Boy*

*Illustrated by Gray Morrow*

# F.W. Woolworth

*Five and Ten Boy*

By Elisabeth P. Myers

THE **BOBBS-MERRILL** COMPANY, INC.
A SUBSIDIARY OF HOWARD W. SAMS & CO., INC.
*Publishers* • INDIANAPOLIS • NEW YORK

LIBRARY OF CONGRESS CATALOG CARD NUMBER: 62-16590

PRINTED IN THE UNITED STATES OF AMERICA

To my son, Tom, without whom I would
never have become acquainted with the
*Childhood of Famous Americans Series*

# Illustrations

*Full pages*

*Numerous smaller illustrations*

# Contents

★   ★   ★

Books by Elisabeth P. Myers

F. W. WOOLWORTH: FIVE AND TEN BOY
KATHARINE LEE BATES: GIRL POET

★ F. W.
Woolworth

*Five and Ten Boy*

# Grandfather's Farm

FRANKIE WOOLWORTH was sitting in the doorway of the little cottage eating a last bite of bread and bacon fat. His two-year-old brother, Charles Sumner, was sitting beside him playing with some colored stones. Inside the house their mother and father were still at the supper table.

It was an August evening in the year 1858, and Frankie was tired. He had been helping his father in the fields all day and his six-year-old muscles were sore.

Suddenly his father's voice rose. "He is going to sell, I tell you! After fifteen years he has had enough of it. He doesn't want to farm any more!"

Frankie's heart began to beat faster. "He" must mean Grandfather Jasper Woolworth, who lived in the main house just up the road. He was the owner of the farm. His son John just managed it for him. John was Frankie's father.

Frankie's mother said something, but she spoke too softly for Frankie to hear. He could guess, though, from what his father said next.

"I can't afford to buy it, Fanny. I wish I could. It is a good farm—that's why he wants so much for it—but you know we don't have that kind of money. We haven't needed it up till now. We had food and lodging right here. The wool money was always enough to buy shoes and sugar——"

Frankie pushed himself a little farther into the house. He wanted to hear everything that was said. After all, he had an interest in the farm, too. He worked hard on it, didn't he? He had mighty sore muscles to prove it, today!

12

"You might borrow some money from my brother," said Fanny Woolworth gently. "He would be glad to help you."

John Woolworth pounded his fist on the table. "I'll just bet he would! Albon McBrier never has thought I was good enough for you. He'd welcome the chance to prove he's a better man than I am!"

Shocked by his father's harsh voice, Frankie turned around so he could see his parents. His mother was standing up now. Her blue eyes were very bright. She ran her hands through her curling, black hair and stamped her foot.

"You have too much pride, John Woolworth!" she cried. "You'd rather uproot us all. Make us leave our home place. Why, your sons were born here! Frank and Charlie—both of them!"

John Woolworth made a noise that could only be called a snort. It sounded to Frankie like the noise the bull made when he was being penned up in the barn. "Home place! A home place belongs to one. This never has!"

"You lived here since you were a very young man," Fanny Woolworth said. "We were married here. You brought me to this cottage on our wedding day——"

John Woolworth passed his big, raw-boned hand over his face. "From the main house to the cottage—a fine wedding trip that was! No wonder the McBriers have a mighty low opinion of your husband!"

Fanny Woolworth went to him and laid her cheek against his head. "Any place a girl goes with the man she marries is a good place," she said. "You have made me very happy here."

John Woolworth sighed so deeply his whole body shook. Frankie had a feeling he shouldn't listen any more, so he eased himself out the door again. Baby Sum was still sitting there, building towers with his colored stones.

14

Frankie picked him up. "Let's go swing, Charles Sumner!" he cried.

With the heavy baby in his arms, he struggled to the rope swing that hung from a branch of the big maple tree. He sat down with the baby on his lap and began to push with one foot. Sum clapped his hands and shouted, "Up! Up!"

Frankie tightened one arm around Sum and grasped the rope with the other hand. He pumped his body back and forth but was careful not to let his feet leave the ground. He didn't want to lose control of the swing, not so long as he was holding his little brother.

"Sing, Frankie, sing!" demanded Sum.

Frankie thought a minute. The only songs he knew were the Irish tunes his mother sang to them at bedtime or those that they sang in church or Sunday school.

"Sing, Frankie, sing!" Sum demanded again.

Frankie began to sing:

"I'm glad I am a Methodist:
I'm mighty proud to be
A member of that pious band
First led by John Wesley!"

"Again!" said Sum.

Frankie laughed. "That's not a good swinging song, Sum. It's better for marching. That's what we do in Sunday school. Want to get down now and march?"

"Swing!" said Sum.

"Then I'll sing something swingy. Listen to this one, Sum!"

"In our work and in our play
Jesus ever with us stay!"

sang Frankie, swinging back and forth in time to his own voice.

Fanny Woolworth came out onto the porch and stood looking at them.

16

Frankie finished the verse and then said loudly, "Time to let the old cat die, Sum!"

He gripped the ground with both feet, holding tightly to Sum as the swing jerked to a stop.

Their mother came out to them and lifted Sum into her arms. Sum pressed his head into the hollow of her shoulder and gave a big yawn.

"Bedtime for Charlie," Fanny Woolworth said.

"Not for me!" said Frankie quickly.

His mother shook her head. "No, not for you. Your father wants to talk to you, Frankie."

Frankie's heart began to pound again. What would Father have to tell him? He watched his mother disappear into the house.

John Woolworth came out in her place. He sat down on the steps and patted a place beside him. "Come here, son," he called.

Frankie walked over and stood in front of his father. This way, the two were at eye level. John Woolworth smiled.

18

"You are getting to be such a big boy, Frankie," he said. "You worked almost as well as a man in the fields today."

"Thank you, Father."

"Yes," his father continued, "you are proving to be 'worth your salt,' as the saying goes."

Frankie smiled at that but said nothing.

"Since that's so, I guess you have a right to know how things stand on this farm. It doesn't belong to us, you know."

"I know. It belongs to Grandfather."

"Yes—and he's going to sell it," John Woolworth said. "Tomorrow is Sunday. You and I are going to start looking for a place of our own."

Frankie tightened his fists. They were going to have to move. Father was not going to ask Uncle Albon for money.

"This place we buy won't be so good as this one," John Woolworth said, "and it won't be so big, but, son—" his voice rose—"it will be ours!"

Frankie let his hands relax. He sat down beside his father on the steps and leaned against him. "All ours!" he said. "That's good, isn't it?"

John Woolworth patted Frankie's shoulder. "I just guess it is, son. When something is yours, you can do what you like with it. That is, so long as you are honest about what you do. Do you understand what I mean?"

"Yes," said Frankie. "Honest means true, doesn't it?"

"That's right. Well—" John Woolworth tightened his arm briefly around Frankie—"you go on to bed. I'll just make sure everything in the barn is quiet. Then I'll turn in, too."

He got up, pulling Frankie up with him. "We'll want to get an early start in the morning," he said.

"Before chores?" asked Frankie hopefully.

"After chores, of course. Your mother will need wood for the stove. The animals must be tended, too, Frankie."

"But before church?"

John Woolworth stood thinking for a minute. "Before church, yes. We'll wear our go-to-meeting clothes. Then if we're not back in Rodman in time, we can look in on a church someplace else."

Frankie looked down at his bare feet. They were very dirty from working all day in the fields. "Does Mother have some hot water on the stove, Father?"

John Woolworth chuckled. "The big tin tub's all ready for you. Saturday night is always bath night, isn't it? You usually try hard enough to forget it, though."

Frankie started for the door. "Tomorrow is special," he said. "Good night, Father."

Next morning, Frankie was up before the old red rooster crowed. He filled the wood box for his mother. He carried oatmeal mash to the chickens. Then he dressed carefully and hurried to the kitchen for breakfast.

Fanny Woolworth filled the plates with crisp fried potatoes, crusty fried eggs, and juicy fried ham. She poured a hot drink made of ground wheat and blackstrap molasses into huge cups.

"Eat hearty, both of you," she said to her son and her husband. "It may be a long drive you'll be taking!"

Frankie and his father smiled at each other. Then John Woolworth bowed his head. Fanny, still standing, did the same. So did Frankie and Baby Sum.

"For what we are about to receive, make us truly thankful," John Woolworth said.

Those were the last words spoken at the table. Eating was a serious business in the farmhouse. Food was needed for the human body just as wood was needed for the stove.

John Woolworth cleaned the last bite off his plate and rose. "I'll put the horses to the wagon," he said to Frankie. "Hurry, now!"

Frankie stuffed his mouth so full he could scarcely chew. He did not dare leave a scrap of food on his plate. "Waste not, want not" was one of John Woolworth's favorite sayings.

Fanny Woolworth started to scold Frankie for his table manners, then thought better of it. She smiled at him instead. "Pick a nice place for us, Frankie," she said. "A pretty place, if you can."

Frankie slid down from his seat. "Whatever it is, it'll be *ours*," he said and hurried out to join his father.

# Five Pennies
# to Spend

Frankie and his father spent many a Sunday looking for a place they could call their own. The old work horses became quite used to plodding along the byways of Jefferson County. Many of the byways were little more than old Indian trails.

One of the best-traveled Indian trails was what was known as the Black River Route. It was along this that John and Frankie Woolworth finally found the spot that seemed to answer all their needs.

The little farm was near the town of Great Bend, New York. It had a view of the river and of thickly wooded hills. Best of all, it was for sale at a price John Woolworth could afford.

The family was all moved and settled before John Woolworth found out why he had been able to buy the place so cheaply. The lovely rolling land was full of rocks. It was not good for growing anything but potatoes and a little pasture grass.

Fanny Woolworth never once complained about the poor choice her husband had made. Instead, she made a special point of finding things she liked about it. "It is pleasant to sit on the porch of an evening," she said, "and to look off to the hills. It's nice to hear the rush and gurgle of the river."

Her brother, Albon McBrier, refused to see anything good about the Woolworth farm. "You will have to scrape along and skimp yourself all the days of your life," he told Fanny one day when he stopped by to visit her.

He did not know that anybody but his sister was around to hear him. Frankie, though, had just come up from the fields for a drink. "No, she won't!" he said. "Someday I'll be as rich as you are, Uncle Albon. Then my mother can sit on the porch and rock all day. She can wear long silk dresses and shoes with real leather tops! You just wait and see!"

Uncle Albon clapped Frankie on the shoulder. "That's the kind of talk I like to hear! This boy of yours has spunk, Fanny. Maybe he *will* be a rich farmer someday!"

Fanny Woolworth smiled at Frankie. "He's a good boy," she said. "He's as good as a hired hand round the place right now."

Frankie's face turned red at his mother's praise. He worked like a hired hand, for sure, but he didn't like the work one bit.

"There's a lot of McBrier in Frankie, all right," Albon McBrier said. "Shouldn't wonder if it'll

26

show up in Sum, too, once he gets big enough to be useful."

Albon McBrier stood up. "I'll be leaving now," he said. He dug into his pocket and brought out a handful of coins. He poked through them and picked out some pennies. "There's a general store as well as a school in Great Bend, isn't there?" he asked Frankie.

Frankie nodded, his eyes on the coins. He had never seen so much money just loose before. "Mr. McNeil's General Store," he said.

"Sure to be some penny candy there," Uncle Albon said. He handed Frankie five pennies. "Licorice whips and lemon drops are the best," he added and winked at Frankie.

Frankie's eyes shone. "Thank you, Uncle Albon! Maybe I can go there after I plant the potatoes tomorrow, Mother?"

Albon McBrier smiled broadly. "Yes, sir! Work before pleasure—that's the ticket!" He went down the steps to where his horse stood waiting. He got easily into the saddle, then waved his hat at Frankie and his mother and rode away.

Late the next afternoon Fanny Woolworth took off her apron and called her two sons. They came running, Frank pulling Sum behind him.

"We've just time to walk to McNeil's Store before I have to start supper," she told them. Her cheeks were pink with the excitement of the little outing, and her eyes were bright. "Go get your pennies, Frankie. Sum and I will start down the road."

Frankie ran to the room he shared with Sum. He had tied the pennies in a bright red bandanna handkerchief and put the bundle under his pillow. He pulled it out now and hurried to catch up with his mother and Sum.

"Red's my favorite color," he said, waving the bandanna in front of his mother. "It's so easy to see, don't you think?"

Fanny Woolworth smiled at him. "It's easy to see and it is a cheerful color, too. Stop waving that bandanna in the air, though, Frankie. Your pennies might fall out!"

Frankie tucked the bandanna into his pocket. He felt so happy that he hopped, skipped, and jumped all the way to McNeil's General Store.

A general store was just what Daniel McNeil kept. He sold goods of all kinds. He sold clothes and tools and food. Great barrels stood all around. One was full of spicy pickles. Another was full of square, salty crackers. A third held dark-brown coffee beans, while a fourth held common household nails.

On one of the counter tops lay a huge round yellow cheese. On another stood jars of sugar and salt and flour. Pots and pans hung on one wall, harness and saddles and horsewhips on another. The smells of leather and spice, of coffee and fresh-starched cloth all blended together.

In the middle of the store was a round, iron stove with chairs pulled up close to it. Mr. McNeil was sitting on one of those chairs when the Woolworths came in. He was reading a newspaper. His square eye-glasses were pushed halfway down his nose. When he saw his customers, he jumped up. The pages of his newspaper scattered all over the floor. Frankie rushed forward to pick them up.

"Mrs. Woolworth, good day!" Daniel McNeil said. "Are these your boys?" He nodded his thanks to Frankie, as the boy put the pages of the paper together and laid it on a chair.

"Yes, they are," said Fanny Woolworth proudly. She pushed Sum forward. "This is Charles Sumner, my youngest."

Frankie stuck out his hand. "I'm Frank Winfield," he said, "but you can call me Frankie."

The storekeeper shook Frankie's hand gravely. "Pleased to meet you," he said. "Now, what can

I do for you today?" he said, looking back at Mrs. Woolworth.

Fanny Woolworth smiled. "Frankie is your customer this afternoon."

Daniel McNeil pointed to a glass display case. "What will it be? A pocketknife? Some marbles?"

"No," said Frankie, though he looked longingly at the knife.

"Want some candy!" Sum piped up.

"That's right," said Frankie. "Some penny candy, please."

"Follow me," said Daniel McNeil. He walked over to another display case. It was full of candy of all sizes and shapes. There were little brown root-beer barrels and green spearmint leaves. There were rainbow-colored jawbreakers that looked like marbles. There were little round red and white peppermints and long fat peppermint sticks. There were spice balls and gumdrops, licorice whips, and lemon drops, too.

31

Sum and Frankie stood there just looking at the candy for quite a few minutes. Both of them kept licking their lips, as if trying to taste the different flavors. Frankie did not know which to choose. Finally he appealed to Mr. McNeil, who had gone behind the counter.

"Is all that *penny* candy?" he asked.

The storekeeper peered at them over the show-case. "Yes-sirree-bob!" he said. "Leastwise, nothing costs *more* than a penny, and some of them con*side*rably less."

Frankie didn't know what "con*side*rably" meant, but he guessed it was a fancy word for "much." "How much less?" he asked, playing his hunch.

"Spearmint leaves, five for a penny. Root-beer barrels the same. Also the lemon drops and jaw-breakers——"

"What about the peppermints and licorice whips?" asked Frankie.

33

"Round peppermints, ten for a penny. They're the best buy of the lot. Peppermint sticks and licorice whips, one penny each."

Frankie tried to keep all the numbers straight by counting on his fingers. He wanted to get the most he could for his five pennies.

"What would give me the most candy?" he asked finally, giving up trying to figure it out for himself. "The most different kinds, I mean. I have five pennies." He untied his red bandanna very carefully and showed Daniel McNeil his money proudly.

The storekeeper opened the sliding doors in the back of the candy case. He took a big pink-and-white-striped bag from a hook. Then he reached in and started to pick out candy.

"Ten peppermints, one penny," he said, dropping them into the bag. "Two root-beer barrels and three spearmint leaves, two pennies. Three jawbreakers and two lemon drops, three pennies.

Two peppermint sticks, two more pennies. Two and three make five. Right, son?"

Frankie knew that much about adding, at least. "Right, sir," he said.

"Want to make any changes?"

"Well—could I make one change? One licorice whip for one peppermint stick?"

Mr. McNeil said yes, then reached back into the case and took out two licorice whips. "These are free," he said, giving one each to Sum and Frankie.

Sum started sucking his right away, but Frankie remembered to say, "Thank you," and to hand Mr. McNeil his precious pennies. "Keeping store must be great fun," he added, watching the storekeeper get out his cash box and put Frankie's pennies safely away.

Daniel McNeil rubbed his hands together. "It's a living," he said.

"Come now, Frankie," Fanny Woolworth said.

"We must hurry home. Your father will be wanting his supper soon now."

They all waved good-by to Mr. McNeil and started for home. Frankie looked back once, just before they rounded the bend that would hide the store from view. Then he looked down at the candy bag clutched tightly in his hand.

"Five cents buys a lot, doesn't it?" he said. He really did not need his mother's answer.

# Boys A'shopping

Snowstorms came early in the season in upper New York State. The first autumn the Woolworths were on their new farm there was a blizzard in October.

"Well," said John Woolworth to his family, "it's lucky we got the hay in!" He looked fondly at Frankie and Sum. "Never could have, without the help of the young ones!"

"They're good boys," agreed their mother.

"So I'll tell you what we're going to do," John Woolworth went on. "I've got a load of wood to sell, so we're all going to Watertown!"

"When? When?" asked the boys together.

"Tomorrow," said their father. "We'll leave bright and early."

Bright and early it was, too, the next morning when they were all settled in the sleigh. Yet, early as it was, others had been on the road before them. When John Woolworth drove out onto the highway, he found the snow already pressed down by the runners of other sleighs.

"Looks like we'll have company at market," he said to his wife. "I was hoping I'd be first with my wood, for once."

"Oh, I hardly think they'll all be ready with their wood," said Fanny Woolworth. "Maybe they're just glad of a chance to rest from chores. Like as not, all they're bringing is a few chickens, some eggs, or maybe late apples."

John Woolworth did not try to answer his wife's brave statement. He knew she was just talking to make him feel better. He turned and tucked the blanket more tightly around her.

38

"Warm enough?" he asked. "Are your feet on the bricks?"

She nodded. "Yes, and the bricks are still hot as can be. I left them on the stove till the very last minute."

John Woolworth looked at her hands, covered by rough wool mittens like his and the boys'. "Maybe this winter I'll get me a raccoon. Then you can have a fur muff for your hands, like the fine ladies we'll see in Watertown!"

"Father!" called Frankie from his seat on top of the potato sacks. "Sum and I want to get off and slide a while!"

John Woolworth pulled on the reins. The horses slowed down and the two boys jumped off into a snowbank at the side of the road. Frank fell face down, but he was laughing as he got to his feet. Snow stuck to his eyelashes and as he blinked he saw a rainbow of colors before the snow melted.

Sum threw a snowball at him. "Hurry up!" he cried. "We're getting left behind!"

Sure enough, the sleigh was moving along down the road. The two boys raced after it. Sometimes they covered long distances by sliding on the smooth tracks worn by the sleigh. For a while a red squirrel ran along with them, chattering excitedly. In the trees beside the road chickadees called to each other. "Chick-a-dee-dee-dee!" the little black-capped birds chirped.

"Chick-a-dee-dee-dee, yourselves!" Frankie called back.

Finally the boys had almost caught up to the sleigh. They could see the clouds the horses' breath made in the cold air.

"Let's get back on!" said Frankie. "We'll want to explore after we get to Watertown."

Watertown was eleven miles from the village of Great Bend. It was the "seat" of Jefferson County, the place where all the business of the county was carried on. Seven thousand people already had their homes there and more were attracted to it every day.

The Public Square, bordered by a wooden sidewalk, was the center of the county's activities. The Courthouse stood in the middle of the Square, and on all sides of it were shops. There were dry-goods, hardware, and grocery stores. There were a bank, a blacksmith's shop, and an open-air market.

It was to the open-air market that farmers like John Woolworth brought their vegetables and wood to sell. They tied their teams to the railing around the Courthouse lawn. The horses would paw the ground and snort as other horses came to stand beside them. The air would be full of the smells of all the things piled in the wagons or sleighs. There would be the scent of fresh-cut wood of many kinds—of pine and fir, of both red and black spruce, of birch and beech and mountain ash. The farmers hoped to sell all of it to the sawmills and papermills that stretched for miles alongside the Black River.

Less strong than the scent of the fresh-cut wood would be the earthy smell of the root vegetables—of potatoes, carrots, and beets—and the mouth-watering smell of the baskets full of apples of all sizes and all shades of red and yellow.

Today John Woolworth pulled up to a good spot right near the entrance walk of the Courthouse. That meant his wares would surely be seen by a great many people. He might get a first-class price for his wood, for once!

Frankie could tell his father was pleased by the quickness of his actions. If he got a poor place, John Woolworth moved slowly, half-beaten before he started. At such times, Frankie did not dare ask to leave before some customers had arrived. Now, though, Frankie and Sum exchanged looks of delight.

"Will you need us, Father?" Frankie asked, as John Woolworth tied up the team.

John Woolworth stroked the velvety-soft nose of one of the horses. "No—you and Sum run along. Don't let Sum fall in the river, Frankie."

"I won't," said Frankie, wondering how his father knew the river would be the place they would head for first.

Feeling free as the breeze that blew around them, Frankie and Sum joined hands and ran for the bridge. Climbing on the railing, they looked down. At this spot there was a waterfall. The Black River tumbled over rocks and fell over a hundred feet to another level. It was this waterfall that provided the power to run the sawmills and paper mills. It was the reason Watertown had been settled in the first place and what gave the place its name.

Frankie reached into his pocket and pulled out some straw he had brought along on purpose. He gave some to Sum. Both of them threw the straw into the water just above where it started to fall. They watched with glee as the straw moved ahead and then dropped into the white-capped waves below. Over and over again they repeated the game, until Frankie was out of straw.

The roar of the waterfall followed them as they walked back toward the Public Square.

"We going to get our boots now?" asked Sum.

Frankie shook his head. "You know better than that, Sum. Can't get boots without money. Can't get money without selling what we brought."

Both boys looked toward the place where the Woolworth sleigh was tied. Their mother was talking to a lady who wore a hoop skirt and a purple bonnet. Beside the lady stood a small boy, carrying a big shopping basket in both hands. He wore a tight coat, buttoned high around his neck, and a black hat that was stiff and looked much like a stovepipe.

"Bet he'd be in trouble if a wind came up," Frankie said, and he put up a hand to feel the cap that fitted snugly over his ears.

"Mother and Father are both busy," said Sum. "Let's go to Carter's."

Carter's was a general store very much like the one in their own village of Great Bend. Like Daniel McNeil's, it offered all the things needed by

45

people for everyday living. Mr. Carter sold work clothes, plain calico cloth to make dresses, farm tools, and kitchen ware. He carried penny candy, too, and a few toys like balls and jacks and jumping ropes.

"Not yet," said Frankie. "We'll be going there later to get our boots. Let's go to the Corner Store now!"

Sum's mouth opened wide. "Oh!" he said. "Do they let farm boys in?"

The full name of the store was Augsbury and Moore's Corner Store, and neither Frankie nor Sum had ever been in it. It was Watertown's biggest and finest dry-goods house. Its customers, also, were Watertown's finest.

Frankie and Sum walked toward the Corner Store. The double doors to it kept opening and closing behind richly dressed customers. The women all wore hoop-skirts like the woman the boys had seen talking to Fanny Woolworth. The

46

men were dressed like the boys in tight-fitting coats and high hats.

"Do they let farm boys in?" asked Sum again.

Frankie watched for a minute. There was no doorkeeper. Why couldn't he and Sum just walk in like anybody else?

"Why not?" asked Frankie. "How will they know we haven't come to buy something?" He took off a mitten and put his hand into his pocket to feel what was there. "I may even do it—if they sell anything for a nickel or six cents. Come on!"

Holding his head high, he pulled at the heavy door. Someone inside helped by pushing it toward him. Frankie and Sum slid through the opening and into the warm store.

There was a soft murmur of voices and the air smelled like flowers. Frankie looked all around, but he couldn't see any flowers anywhere. Sum crept very close to him and held on to his sleeve.

They started down the main aisle. All of a sud-

47

den they couldn't hear voices any more. They just heard the *clop-clop* of their rough boots. They stopped walking and then the voices began again.

A woman came from behind a counter and spoke to them. "May I serve you?" she asked.

Frankie looked at her. She was very pretty. Her hair was piled high on her head and she wore a high lace collar fastened with a little black bow. "I—I thought maybe I could find something for my mother," he said.

Somebody laughed, and Sum tugged at Frankie's sleeve again. "Let's go!" he whispered.

"Some French gloves, perhaps?" asked the woman. "Some perfumed soap? We have some that smells just like lilies of the valley."

Frankie looked at Sum. So *that* was what smelled like flowers! What about soap like that for his mother? Frankie thought about her for a minute. She always smelled clean—like sheets blowing in the wind or like the yellow soap she

48

used to wash them. Did he *want* her to smell like flowers instead?

"Not soap," he said, and looked at the woman closely. "A piece of black ribbon, maybe, like you're wearing?"

The woman touched her throat. "Like this?" she asked. "This comes by the yard only—and costs just twenty-five cents."

"Twenty-five cents!" said Frankie. "I don't have that much!"

Again there was laughing all around. The woman looked cross. "Then go to Carter's Store," she said. "This ribbon is silk. Your mother probably wouldn't feel right wearing it, anyway!"

Frankie's eyes blazed. "My mother's prettier than you are!" he said. "She's politer, too. *She* wouldn't make a farm boy feel out of place, if she were in *your* shoes!"

The woman turned red and looked all around her. The people were laughing at her now, Frankie realized, and he was glad. "Come on, Sum," he said to his little brother. "Let's go over to Carter's Store."

Eyes straight ahead, he walked toward the door. Someone hurried to open it for him, and soon he and Sum were out in the cold again.

Frankie was very quiet for a few minutes. He breathed quickly, drawing in great gulps of fresh air. Just before they reached Carter's he pounded one fist into the palm of his other hand.

"There ought to be a store," he said, "where nobody bothers you. Where you can walk up and down until you see something you want. If you don't see anything, you oughta be free to walk out again. Right, Sum?"

Clearly Sum didn't know. "Here's Carter's," he said. "Let's look at boots."

# Frankie Meets Miss Penniman

ONE MORNING early in December Frankie and Sum were sitting at the kitchen table. Frankie was showing Sum how to make a wooden whistle. He had just put the whistle up to his lips to try it when he heard the front door knocker.

The boys looked at each other. No one they knew ever came to the front door. Who in the world could their visitor be?

Frankie knew his mother was upstairs. She was putting fresh feathers into cotton sacks that, when stuffed, would be pillows for the family.

Frankie called up to her. "Mother! Someone's at the front door!"

The horseshoe that served as a door knocker clanged again.

"Go see who's there!" Fanny Woolworth answered. Her voice sounded strange, but Frankie knew why. She was talking through closed teeth. She didn't want to get feathers in her mouth. "Tell whoever it is I can't come just now."

Frankie raced across the kitchen, through the sitting room, and down the hall to the front door. Sum was close behind him. They pulled and twisted the seldom used doorknob. At last the latch clicked and the door opened.

A young lady stood there smiling at them. She wore a heavy woolen shawl, a checked wool skirt, and a brown velvet bonnet. "Hello!" she said.

"Hello!" said Frankie.

The young lady looked behind the boys into the hall. "Is your mother at home?" she asked.

Frankie nodded. "She can't come to the door, though," he said. "She's making feather pillows."

The visitor nodded in understanding. "I am Miss Emma Penniman, the schoolteacher," she said. "May I come in and talk to you and your mother for a few minutes?"

Frankie didn't know what to do. He had never been faced with such a question before.

"You'll catch cold, standing in the doorway like that," Miss Penniman said.

Frankie made up his mind. "You can come in."

He stepped aside, shoving Sum back too. Miss Penniman came in and Frankie shut the door behind her. She stamped her feet free of snow. Then she bent down to remove her rubber overshoes. Frankie and Sum stared as she took them off and showed neat little low leather shoes.

"Is there someplace we can sit down?" Miss Penniman asked.

Frankie led the way into the parlor. That was a room used only for very special visitors. It had a fireplace that had never known a fire. In it, instead of wood, was a lace-paper fan. In the middle of the room was a round table with the family *Bible* lying on it. The chairs and the sofa were all stiff and stuffed with horsehair.

Miss Penniman took off her shawl and laid it on the sofa. Then she bunched her skirt carefully behind her and sat down. When Frankie, too, sat down he found out why she had done so. The horsehair pricked! He wiggled uncomfortably.

"This is a very pretty parlor," said Miss Penniman, with a smile.

"My mother brought everything in it when she married my father," said Frankie. "There's lots more furniture like this at my Uncle Albon's. He lives at Pillar Point."

Miss Penniman nodded. "Ah, yes. I met your Uncle Albon. That's why I'm here today."

Frankie's eyes opened wide. That *was* news!

"He thinks it is high time you were attending my school."

Frankie smiled broadly. "I think so, too! I was going to start last spring, when we finished our planting. When I was ready, though, the term was over."

Miss Penniman's face reddened. "We had to close school early," she said, "because there were not any more families who were willing to give me bed and food."

In all country towns the custom about teachers was the same. They were paid very little, and they "boarded around." A teacher would live for a week or a month with one pupil's family and then move on to another's. The school term ran from six weeks to four or five months. Its length depended entirely on how long there was someone willing to "take care of" the teacher.

"Mr. McBrier thought your family would be willing to take me for a while this winter," Miss Penniman went on, smiling at Frankie. "Then you and I could walk to school together."

Sum quickly got tired of hearing Frankie and the visitor talk about school. He got down from his seat and left the room. In a few minutes, Fanny Woolworth arrived to take his place.

Fanny Woolworth's face was pink with hurrying. Sum had come to her with the news of the visitor in the parlor. Hastily she had tied a knot in the last pillow case. Then, not stopping to look at herself in the cracked mirror of the dresser, she had come straight down the stairs. She could not know she had a curly feather caught in her hair. She wondered briefly why Frankie looked at her so oddly when she entered the room.

The visitor rose gracefully to her feet and smiled at her hostess. "I am Emma Penniman," she said.

Fanny Woolworth smiled, too. "Sit down again, please," she said, and took a chair herself. "I am sorry I could not greet you at the door. I hope Frankie explained."

"Oh, yes," said Miss Penniman. "Frankie and I have had a fine time getting acquainted, too. Haven't we, Frankie?"

Frankie had a hard time getting his mind off the feather that was caught in his mother's hair.

"Frankie!" said his mother. "Miss Penniman spoke to you."

Frankie jumped. "Oh!" he said, trying to think what the teacher might have said. "I think it would be nice to have Miss Penniman with us!"

Fanny Woolworth frowned, but Miss Penniman laughed. "That's a good enough answer to my question, Mrs. Woolworth," she said.

The answer had set Fanny Woolworth's mind to working. The question of "putting up teacher" had to be faced, if Frankie was to attend school. Still, she could not invite Miss Penniman without John Woolworth's permission.

"Frankie, please see if you can find your father," she said. "I think he's in the barn."

Frankie passed close by his mother on the way out of the room. Quickly he stroked his hand over her hair and removed the feather. She felt only the soft touch of his hand and put up her own to pat his. Frankie looked at Miss Penniman. She was looking at him with understanding in her eyes. He felt a warm glow all through his body. He was going to like his schoolteacher!

Miss Penniman came to live with the Woolworth family right away. Every day she and Frankie walked to school together.

The school was a small, one-room stone building. It stood on a rise of land. A few oak trees near by gave shade when they were in leaf. One side of the schoolyard was known as the "boys' side." Here bases were laid for ball games in the springtime and there was a pile of stones for playing "Duck On the Rock." The other side of the schoolyard was the "girls' side." Small flat rocks and bushes made furniture and walls for the girls to play house. Small trees, easily spaced, were ideal for their game of tree tag. The boys and girls never played together, though they were in the same room together all term long.

Inside the school at the front was the teacher's desk. Beside it were two "blackboards." They were wide boards nailed together and covered with black oilcloth. The children's desks were built for two and were of different sizes. Pupils of every age had to share the same room and the same teacher. Sometimes even babies three years old were sent to school, just to get them out from under their mothers' feet.

The school day followed the same pattern week after week. First, Miss Penniman read a chapter from the *New Testament*. Next, the children recited the Lord's Prayer together. Then it was time for singing.

Frankie liked to sing, but until he went to school all he had heard were church hymns or bedtime songs. The very first morning he sat at a desk, Miss Penniman played a tune he had never heard.

"What's that?" he whispered to his seat mate.

"The tune's 'Yankee Doodle,'" came the answer, "but we sing different words to it."

Miss Penniman looked up when she heard the whispering. When she realized the sound came from Frankie's seat she frowned but said nothing. She finished playing the introduction and then nodded. All the children began to sing:

"There is a time to come to school;
'Tis when the bell is ringing.
There is a time to read and write,
Also a time for singing."

Frankie was eager to learn, but he soon discovered that for most of the children the school day centered around two pails—the water pail and the dinner pail.

The water pail sat on a bench near the door

with a tin dipper beside it. Just above it was a shelf for holding the dinner pails.

Going after water was the great treat of the morning. Whoever was allowed the honor took the pail to the nearest neighbor's well. On pleasant days, it sometimes took a long time for the water boy to complete his errand.

Passing the water was also a highly popular pastime. The dipper held a quart—four cupfuls. The passer went from seat to seat with it. Everyone drank from the same dipper. When it was empty, the passer filled it again and continued until every child had had a drink. That job, too, could be dragged out to waste time.

At dinnertime excitement always ran high. What did each one have in his pail? Part of the fun was to trade sight unseen. The owner opened his dinner pail just a crack. According to what smells came out through the opening, trading was heavy or slow. The smell of dill pickles or of

beans baked in molasses was easy to guess, but
nearly all of the pupils had those in their pails.
The real sport lay in guessing who had something
extra, like applesauce cake or doughnuts.

Frankie was lucky, though, in having Miss
Penniman as his teacher. She had no more than
eighth-grade education herself, but she loved to
teach. Since Frankie also wanted to learn, she
went out of her way to help him. Walking home
over the frozen fields that very first week, they
recited the "Lumberman's Alphabet" together:

> "A is for axes, you very well know.
> B for the boys who can swing it also.
> C is for chopping so early begun.
> D is for the danger we oft-times do run.
> E is for echo that through the woods rang.
> F is the foreman who headeth our gang.
> G is the grindstone, so swift it does turn.
> H is the handle, so smooth it was worn——"

and kept step to its rhythm as they walked.

# A Friend of Napoleon

FRANKIE'S HERO was Napoleon Bonaparte. A life of Napoleon was one of the first books Miss Penniman had given Frankie to read. He had enjoyed it so much, she had told him to keep the book if he wished. Now he was seldom without it. Luckily it was small, since he kept it in the pocket of his jeans where it would be handy when he wanted it.

Frankie was interested in Napoleon for several reasons. Napoleon, like Frankie, had been a poor boy, and look how he had advanced in the world! He had made up his mind to be Emperor of the French—and he was. "You get what you want if you try hard enough" had been his belief, and it was one Frankie decided to adopt.

More than that, though, Frankie was interested in Napoleon because of his connection with Upper New York State. The actual connection was through his brother, Joseph Bonaparte.

Joseph Bonaparte was Napoleon's favorite brother. When Napoleon was Emperor of France, his power was so great he was able to make Joseph, first, King of Naples, then King of Spain. After the Battle of Waterloo, when Napoleon was dethroned, Joseph fled to the United States, taking the Spanish crown jewels with him. He made his way to Upper New York, where James LeRay de Chaumont, an exiled Frenchman, was waiting to receive him. De Chaumont had bought thousands of acres in Jefferson and Lewis counties in 1802.

Using the title "Count de Survilliers" instead of his own name, Joseph gave De Chaumont a hundred and twenty thousand dollars' worth of jewels in exchange for a hundred and fifty thousand acres of land in Lewis and Jefferson counties. He had many houses built for him on this property. One, at Natural Bridge, was called the cup-and-saucer house because of its shape.

The cup-and-saucer house was octagonal—eight-sided—and the walls were bored for gunsights. It had a rounded roof with a cupola, or lookout tower, on top. Joseph intended it as a hideout for his brother Napoleon, if the ex-Emperor could escape from Saint Helena, the island on which he was a prisoner of war.

The cup-and-saucer house still stood at Natural Bridge, near Cape Vincent village. One June morning, when John Woolworth announced that he was going to drive that way to a sale, Frankie asked his father to let him and Sum go along.

"I'd have to leave you there for hours," objected John Woolworth. "I've got money together to buy a bull, and I'm not going to buy one till I see every one that comes in for sale. 'Sides that, I'm going to take along some butter your mother's made in fancy shapes. I promised her, if it brought enough, I'd buy her a setting hen. Might be dark before I came for you."

"Please, Father," said Frankie. "You know how much I've wanted to see the place 'Joe Nap' fixed up for the Emperor."

"Joe Nap" was the pet name by which Joseph Bonaparte had been known to the country folk. He had spent money freely, given work to many, and paid high wages. The shortened name suited him, they felt, because he was a short, stout man.

"Once you've seen it, then what will you do?" asked John Woolworth.

"Well, then—then we'll walk cross-country, where the French used to ride horseback or, maybe, if you're going to be *very* late——" Frankie stopped and looked pleadingly at his father.

"If I'm going to be *very* late—what will you do then, Frankie?"

"We'll walk to Lake Bonaparte."

John Woolworth looked at Frankie's pink, excited face. "I guess I'm going to take longer than I thought," he said.

While her menfolk had been talking, Fanny Woolworth had been making sandwiches for Frankie and Sum to take along in their pockets. She cut thick slices from a loaf of bread that was still hot from the oven. She spread them with some of the maple sugar Uncle Albon had brought her fresh-made from the sap of his own maple trees.

She handed the sandwiches to Frankie and Sum when they got up from the table.

"None for me?" asked John Woolworth.

Fanny Woolworth patted her husband's arm. "Go along with you!" she said. "You know you'll be asked to break bread with any number of people at the sale." By that, she meant there would be farm women setting out lunches, and one of them was sure to want to share the food with a man there by himself. That was a custom well understood in the North Country, and John Woolworth, indeed, had just been making a gentle joke when he asked, "None for me?"

John Woolworth left the boys in Cape Vincent village and drove away. Frankie and Sum looked at each other. Neither had been left alone before like this, and suddenly they felt very strange.

"Well," said Frankie, "we can't just stand here. I wonder where the cup-and-saucer house is."

They began to walk, looking around them as they went. The village seemed much like others they had visited. The streets were tree-lined, and one-family frame houses were built close to the brick sidewalks. Some of the houses had small garden plots that were freshly spaded and fenced in behind white pickets. The smell of the damp earth was pleasant to the two farm boys. Frankie bent down and pushed his hand through an opening in one of the fences. He picked up a clod of dirt and crumbled it between his fingers. It felt cool and familiar to him, though it was better soil by far than any on the Woolworth farm.

"Now your hand is dirty," said Sum.

Frankie looked all around. The time was still quite early for anyone but a farmer, and nobody was watching them. He stooped and rubbed his hand against the dew-wet grass. Then he wiped it against his jeans and smiled at Sum.

"What are you *enfants* doing?" a man's voice called to them.

*Enfants* was the French word for "children," but Frankie didn't know that. He thought perhaps it meant something bad, like "rascal."

"N-nothing!" he said, and moved closer to little Sum.

The owner of the voice came across the street

to them. He wore a dove-gray suit with tight-fitting trousers and a high, black silk hat. At his neck was a black scarflike tie, fastened with a jewel-encrusted stick pin. Frankie stared at the pin, wondering if the jewels were real.

"Are you lost?" asked the man.

"N-no, sir," said Frankie. "We're looking for the cup-and-saucer house, that's all."

The man took off his hat and bowed to the boys. "Armand d'Anjou, at your service," he said.

When Frankie just looked confused, D'Anjou smiled. "In America, any friend of Napoleon's is a friend of mine," he said. "Follow me."

Frankie and Sum followed their guide until he stopped by what could only be the cup-and-saucer house. It looked just as it was described in the *Farmer's Almanac.*

"Would you like to go inside?" asked D'Anjou.

Too overcome at the idea to speak, Frankie and Sum just nodded, so Armand d'Anjou knocked twice on the heavy oak door. Frankie just had time enough to notice that the Bonaparte coat of arms was carved on the doorpost before the door was opened.

Inside, some of the rich furnishings still remained. The downstairs, D'Anjou explained, had been where Joseph Bonaparte and his followers had lived. The upstairs had been reserved for Napoleon, and thus had never been used. There the walls were still hung with red silk draperies, embroidered all over with gold imperial crowns. A few slim chairs stood against the walls, and they, too, were covered with red silk.

Frankie took a deep breath, as if he could draw the wonder of it all deep into his lungs. "I knew red was my favorite color," he said in a hushed voice, "but now I know why!"

# Methodist
# Camp Meeting

AFTER LEAVING the cup-and-saucer house, Frankie was so enchanted that he hardly remembered what else he had planned to do with his day off. Sum, though, had felt uneasy in the strange surroundings, and he was glad to be outdoors again.

"Where's Lake Bonaparte?" he asked Armand d'Anjou, when Frankie didn't speak up.

D'Anjou waved an arm in the general direction they should take. "Don't expect to find anything like *this* there," he said, and nodded back toward the cup-and-saucer house. "In fact, you'll likely run into a church camp meeting. That's a far cry from anything *Napoleon* ever attended!"

"We don't have to attend anything," said Frankie, alerted by the sound of Napoleon's name. "The lake's still there, isn't it?"

D'Anjou nodded. "It still looks much as it must have to Joseph's friends when they rode on it in his Venetian swan boat."

"Well," said Frankie, his eyes still dreamy, "we'll have to see it. Thank you, sir."

Once again, D'Anjou took off his tall silk hat and bowed to the boys. "Au revoir," he said.

Frankie and Sum started along the dirt path that had held the hoof prints of the Frenchmen's horses. In the fields on all sides of them, pink wild roses were just coming into bloom. Their perfume scented the air, and over them the honeybees buzzed. In among the roses great dandelions grew, some of them a foot tall, their round heads as big as dollar pieces. Frankie picked one of the dandelions and held it under Sum's chin.

"How much do you like butter, Sum?" he teased, rubbing the weed against Sum's soft skin.

Some of the pollen—a yellow dust—from the plant stuck to Sum, and Frankie laughed. "You really like it!" he said. "Better watch out, or you'll be more of a butterball than you are already!"

Sum batted Frankie's hand away. "Stop that!" he said. "I'd rather be like me than a long string bean like you!"

Frankie dropped the dandelion. "Don't be mad, Sum," he said. He looked down at the path their feet were following. "Let's pretend we're Frenchies, invited to Joe Nap's hunting lodge to spend the day."

"Oh, all right," said Sum, but he waited for Frankie to take the lead in the game. In that way the two were much like the Bonaparte brothers. Napoleon always led, and Joseph always followed.

Frankie picked up a stick and beat against his

76

leg. "Giddap," he cried, as if to a horse. "I'm tired of being in the saddle. Giddap!"

He began to run in a galloping manner. Sum copied him, beating his leg and shouting, "Giddap!" too. Before long, they came to some trees and soon they were walking in a real forest.

"We must be getting close," said Frankie. "The lake was in the woods." Pretending once more, he added, "Pretty soon we ought to hear the sound of music! Joe Nap used to have an orchestra floating in a barge on the lake. They played to entertain his guests, while they ate their dinners off gold plates."

Much to Frankie's surprise, they did hear music very shortly. It wasn't the whine of violins, though—it was the sound of a trumpet. Frankie stopped so suddenly that Sum crashed into him.

"Must be the camp meeting Mr. D'Anjou told us about," said Frankie.

Sum turned around. "Let's go back," he said.

Frankie grabbed Sum's arm. "Not till I see what's going on!"

"You said we didn't have to attend any meeting," cried Sum. "Sunday church is enough!"

"It won't hurt to look," said Frankie.

They walked on, and soon they came to a clearing. Lake Bonaparte was there, all right, but beside it was a sight never dreamed of by French noblemen. Hundreds of tents were pitched toward the outer edges of the area, their snowy whiteness showing up against the deep green of the tall trees. Beyond them were all the wagons which had brought the people to the meeting. Hundreds of horses were tied to trees near by. Cook-fires were burning in front of nearly every tent. The smell of chickens roasting and hams boiling made both boys' mouths water.

Frankie dug into his pockets and pulled out the sandwiches he had almost forgotten. "Here," he said, shoving one into Sum's hand.

The trumpet sounded again, and crowds of people streamed from the camp area toward the lake. Chewing their sandwiches, Frankie and Sum followed them.

The meeting place took up an enormous area of ground beside the lake. Most of the area was fitted with rough boards set up about a foot off the ground and serving as benches. At one end, facing the benches, was a pulpit, or preacher's stand. In front of it a space was railed off and covered with straw.

Frankie and Sum sat down with the crowd and waited to see what would happen next. For a few moments there was such a complete silence that Frankie could hear the lapping of the lake water against the shore. Then a tall man with deep-set eyes got up and walked to the pulpit.

"Welcome to the House of the Lord," he said.

"Amen," said the people as one voice.

"We're here today to sing together, laugh together, and pray together," the preacher said. "Before we do anything else, let's all shake hands. Everyone shake hands with his neighbors— those in front, those beside, those behind!"

With a great creaking of boards, everyone did as the preacher asked. Frankie and Sum, caught up in the spirit of fellowship, joined in.

"That's fine!" said the preacher. "Now that everybody's a friend of everybody else, let's sing about the best Friend of all!"

At the top of his voice, he sang out the first words of the hymn, "What a Friend We Have in Jesus!" and the crowd took it up and continued with the song. Frankie joined in happily, and after a minute Sum did, too. It was fun to sing as loud as they liked!

The hymn ended, and once again the preacher held up his hand for silence. When everything was still again, he said, " 'I am the Way and the Truth and the Light, saith the Lord.' "

80

"Amen," said the crowd.

"Yesterday," the preacher went on, "many men and women saw the Light. Today let's hear from some of the children. 'Suffer the little children to come unto me,' Jesus said. Suppose we start with the boy in the blue suit——"

Everybody stared at the boy in a blue suit at one end of the third bench. His face was buried in his hands.

"Come forward and be counted, son," the preacher urged.

The boy walked slowly toward the railing by the pulpit and knelt in the straw. He threw back his head and said, "I've told lies. I've swiped things. I've picked fights with lads younger than me, just to show them I was boss."

Frankie held his breath. That boy wasn't much older than he was! How did he dare get up and tell his sins to everybody?

The preacher held out his arms toward the

81

boy. In a minute the lad got up and walked forward and grasped the preacher's hands.

"I've found Jesus, and now I won't do those things any more!"

"Hallelujah!" shouted the people.

Frankie's heart pounded when the boy turned to face the crowd. What a brave thing he had done! How contented he looked!

Just then a stout man in front of Frankie stood up and shouted, "Let us march on to victory while the enemy, Evil, is in retreat!" He began to sing:

"We're marching to Zion,
Beautiful, beautiful Zion,
We're marching upward to Zion,
The beautiful city of God!"

The people in the first row got up and began to march, each one holding onto the one ahead of him. Soon everybody was up, singing, "We're marching to Zion!" as they marched around the area. Every time they came to the end of a verse, the stout man shouted, "Keep singing!"

Sum marched with them for a while, then dropped out and went to sit down under a tree near the lake. He was tired out.

When Frankie noticed that Sum was gone, he was cold with fright. How long ago had Sum left? Had he tried to go back to Cape Vincent alone? Suppose he got lost in the woods!

Shaking himself free of the hand on his shoulder, Frankie moved out of the crowd. He looked at the benches and the "sinner's bench" near the pulpit. Then he walked down to the lake and soon found the child.

Sum had his feet in the water, splashing them up and down to make little waves. Frankie sat down beside him and stuck his feet into the lake, too. The water felt cool and good.

"I'd like to put all of me into the lake," Frankie said. "I was pretty warm back there."

He looked long and hard at the lake by which ex-King Joe had plotted to set up a new empire. Finally he said, "We came to see Lake Bonaparte. We've seen it. Now we can go home."

"Amen," said Sum, and both boys laughed.

# Rid of the Hoe

ONE DAY in the fall of 1864, Albon McBrier drove a wagon up to the Woolworth farm. Frankie was busy in the yard, digging a hole for a tiny maple tree he had brought from the woods. He waved to his uncle, but kept on with his work.

Uncle Albon got down from his high seat. He walked over to Frankie and looked at the hole.

"Leave room to spread the roots," he said.

"There's room," said Frankie, lifting the tree and settling it into the hole. "Hand me the water pail, please, Uncle."

Instead, Uncle Albon poured the water himself, until the hole was full.

"I've a load of food I promised to deliver to Madison Barracks," he said then, while Frankie pressed loose dirt around the tree. "Want to drive to Sackets Harbor with me?"

Frankie stood up and brushed mud off his hands. "I'll change my shirt and tell Mother I'm going," he said, starting for the house.

"Tell her I'll have you back in time for the evening chores," his uncle called after him. "I'm not one to let a lad shirk his duty."

Frankie's shoulders sagged. "Duty!" he muttered to himself. "That's what farm chores are!"

Frankie had never liked farm work, though he always tried to do the very best he could. The time wasn't so very far off when he'd have to leave school. He would be thirteen on his next birthday. When he was sixteen, he would be expected to start earning his own living. What did he know about *any* work but farming?

Fanny Woolworth was standing at the kitchen

table when Frankie came in. She had her hands in bread dough, kneading it with her strong fists. Frankie sniffed, enjoying the smell of fresh yeast that rose in the warm air.

"Uncle Albon's here, Mother," he said. "Wants me to drive to Sackets Harbor with him—to Madison Barracks, that is."

Fanny Woolworth looked at her son. Her blue eyes sparkled. "I used to go to balls at Madison Barracks when I was a girl," she said.

"Balls? You mean—*dancing?*"

Fanny Woolworth's face turned pink. "I wasn't a Methodist in those days," she said. She tossed her head. "Anyway, I can't see there's anything sinful in dancing!"

Frankie didn't know what to say. Certainly his *mother* wasn't a sinner!

"I don't imagine there's much dancing there now," she said, coming to his rescue. "After all, there is a war going on!"

Frankie thought about that as he put on his clean shirt. He was still thinking about it when he climbed up to the high seat beside his uncle. The War Between the States had begun the day before his ninth birthday. Now, three and a half years later, it was still, as his mother said, "going on." He forgot about it for days at a time, since people seldom talked about it.

"What kind of food are you taking to the army, Uncle Albon?" Frankie asked.

"Salt pork, potatoes, onions," answered his uncle. "Stuff to stick to their ribs."

Sackets Harbor was west of Watertown at the eastern end of Lake Ontario. The army post occupied the east line of the little village. As Uncle Albon drove past the heavy gate, Frankie saw at once why the place was called Madison Barracks. The rows of brick and stone buildings *were* the army post. They came together to form a parade ground—and that was all.

While Albon McBrier tended to the business of delivering the food, another soldier showed Frankie around the post.

"That's where General Grant had his quarters," the soldier said, pointing at some windows in one of the buildings.

Frankie didn't know much about the "goings on" down South, but he had heard of General Grant. "What was General Grant doing here?" he asked, amazed.

The young soldier laughed. "He wasn't fighting the war then," he said. "He lived here in 1848—brought his bride here after the honeymoon and stayed for six months."

"Oh," said Frankie.

"Came back for a year in 1851, too!" the soldier continued. "He's *our* general—and all of us are itching to get down there and join him. You can bet your boots on that!" His face, which had lighted up so when he spoke of "our general," turned suddenly sober. "Probably the war will be over, though, before *I* get a chance to get in it!"

Frankie swallowed hard. "You really *want* to get into the fight?"

"Sure do!" said the soldier. "Don't you?"

"Me? I'm too young. I'm only twelve!"

"Boys younger than you are trying to get into action every day the war goes on," the soldier said. "They lie about their ages. They hide in troop trains—anything, just to be a part of things down there."

"Do some of them make it?" asked Frankie.

"Sure—as drummer boys, water boys, army aides. Sure they do."

"They're really part of the *army* then?"

The soldier nodded. "They're just the lads who'll make a life for themselves in the army. They trade their hoes for guns. Can you blame them for not wanting to trade back?"

Frankie shook his head. No, he couldn't blame them. Goodness knows, he'd really like to get rid of *his*—the potato hoe in particular!

Albon McBrier came back shortly, his business done, and he and Frankie headed for home. During the next weeks, as Frankie worked with the potatoes, he often thought of his talk with the young soldier. Then, when in April of the next year General Lee surrendered to General Grant at Appomattox Courthouse, Frankie thought of it again. Had the soldier moved on to join "our general," or had the war ended too soon? What about the boys who had traded their hoes for guns? Were they back on the farms now, or had they broken away for good?

The chance to break away—that was what Frankie felt he simply had to have. The trouble was, he wasn't fitted for anything but farming. What other occupations were open to him with his lack of education?

He kept his eyes open, hoping for an idea. One day, he went with his father to the railroad round-house in Watertown. There he saw the great engines of the Rome, Watertown, and Ogdens-burg Railroad. He heard the shrill whistles, the clang as the cars were coupled. He smelled the thick smoke that puffed into the clear air and felt the hot steam that swished out from under the enormous engines.

"Maybe I can be a trainman!" he thought then.

Another time, he visited a big lumber camp with Uncle Albon. He ate dinner with the men. They were huge, healthy fellows, and they talked together as if they thought their life was the most wonderful in the world. The room rang with their booming laughter as they served themselves mightily.

"Maybe if I ate as much as they do, I'd be huge, too," thought Frankie, looking at the enor-mous helpings of baked beans, smoked beef, and pie on the lumbermen's plates. "Maybe then I could be a lumberman, myself!"

As the time for him to leave school came nearer and nearer, Frankie talked to his father about other jobs than farming. He never came right out and said he didn't want to be a farmer, though, so John Woolworth couldn't know how discouraging his remarks were to his son.

"Railroading and lumbering are mighty wearing, son," he said. "They need muscle men—not tall, thin fellows like you. You'd better recognize when you're well off." He clapped Frankie on the back. "Farming's something you can do, as I should very well know."

Miss Penniman knew that the boy dreaded coming to the end of his school days. She also knew, from things he had said, that his heart was not really in the farm work he did. During the winter of 1867-1868, while she was living with the Woolworths, she decided to help

94

Frankie with his problems. She talked often to Fanny Woolworth, feeling sure that Frankie's mother could be made to understand.

"Frankie is a smart boy," Miss Penniman said one day, when she was helping Fanny Woolworth peel apples for pie. "He knows the value of following through on any job he undertakes."

"Frankie's a good boy," agreed Fanny Woolworth proudly.

"He could go far, if he had more schooling."

"He's had as much as you've had, now," Fanny Woolworth reminded her. "Isn't that good enough for him, too?"

Miss Penniman shook her head. "Not if he ever wants to do something more demanding than farming," she said gently.

Fanny Woolworth looked closely at the teacher. "He wants something more, does he?" she asked, as their eyes met. "That's what you've been trying to tell me, isn't it?"

Before Miss Penniman could answer, they both heard the tootle of a flute. The flute was Frankie's newest possession, and he carried it with him, playing it whenever he had a spare moment. He was not a very good flutist, but he loved to make music for himself.

"He's not an ordinary boy," Miss Penniman said. "He ought to have a chance to prove it."

Fanny Woolworth nodded. "He'll have the chance. I promise you."

Frankie came in then, his face aglow with the pleasure music always gave him.

"Been playing to the cows?" his mother teased.

Frankie laughed. "They like hearing me now. I sometimes think they give more milk after I've played to them!"

The two women laughed with him at the idea. Frankie put his flute into its case and put it up on a shelf out of harm's way. Then he helped himself to an apple and took a big, crunching bite.

Fanny Woolworth stirred cinnamon and sugar into a bowl of apple slices. "We've been talking about your future, Frankie," she said.

Frankie looked from her to Miss Penniman. His teacher gave him an encouraging nod, and he felt suddenly hopeful.

"I *will* be sixteen my next birthday, won't I?" he said cautiously.

Fanny Woolworth's eyes flashed. "Don't pretend with me!" she said. "I'm being serious!"

Frankie put his arm around her shoulders and hugged her a little. "I'm sorry," he said.

"Listen to Miss Penniman a minute," she went on. "I think she may have an idea that will help."

Both of them turned toward the teacher now. She looked a little taken aback, now that the problem was given to her to solve.

"Well," she said, clutching the apple knife tightly for support, "you *could* go to the Commercial College in Watertown, Frank."

The use of the name "Frank" instead of "Frankie" startled both the Woolworths for a moment, but of course Frank was too old for the baby name now.

He stood up straight and squared his shoulders. "I could study bookkeeping," he said, growing excited at the thought. "You've always said I was good at figures. Then I could— why, I could get a job in some store, couldn't I?"

"Would you *want* to work in a store?" asked Fanny Woolworth.

Frank's eyes shone. "That's what I've *always* wanted," he said. "I just didn't know it!"

# No Shopkeepers

On April 13, 1868, Frank became sixteen. Of course, that fact did not mean he had to quit school overnight. He would be allowed to finish out the term, but that gave him only a few weeks. By May 1, all farm children were needed to help with spring planting, so school always "let out" then, too.

Now, though, Frank had his mother as an ally. She knew he did not want to be a "full-time farmer" like his father. In a way, she was glad. Unlike John Woolworth, she thought a farmer's life was very hard—as hard, any day, as a lumberman's or a railroad man's.

On the night of Frank's birthday, after he had gone to bed, Fanny Woolworth went to the barn to talk to her husband. She knew he was there, mending a harness that had broken that day. As she stepped inside, one of the horses whinnied, blowing her a soft greeting. John Woolworth looked up.

"Something wrong?" he asked, for she seldom came to the barn.

Fanny shook her head. Her husband drew up a milking stool.

"Sit down," he invited her.

Turning up the bottom of her long skirt so it wouldn't drag on the floor, she sat down beside him. Neither spoke for a few minutes. John Woolworth kept on with his work of sewing the two pieces of leather harness together. Finished, he cut the heavy thread with a knife. The snap of the cut sounded quite loud in the quiet barn.

"Finished?" asked Fanny Woolworth.

100

"With this," he said, hanging the harness on a nail near the horse's stall. "Have a whip to re-braid," he added. "Might as well do it, long as you're here to talk to."

Fanny Woolworth pulled her woolen shawl more closely around her, though the barn was quite warm with heat from the animals' bodies.

"Something on your mind?" her husband asked, his fingers busy again. "Could it be Frank, maybe?"

Fanny Woolworth looked startled. "What makes you ask that?"

"What would be more natural? It's the boy's birthday, isn't it? An important birthday, too," he added, and he smiled. "Leastwise, so the school board thinks!"

"Frank's liked school," she answered. "Every minute of it."

"I know—don't think I'm not grateful for his learning, either. He's much better at figuring than I am—better at the business end all around. I expect to get top prices for things, with him handling the marketing."

Fanny Woolworth's heart skipped a beat at her husband's speaking the word "business." He had given her a natural opening for what she had to say. "He could go to the Commercial

College in Watertown," she said. "Then he'd know still more about——"

Her voice broke off as John Woolworth's face darkened. "Albon been putting you up to this?" he said. "He'd like nothing better than getting Frank to work for *him,* I suppose."

"No!" Fanny Woolworth said. "Albon had nothing to do with it."

"Well, then," said her husband, the tone of his voice still icy, "he won't be putting up the money for more schooling, will he?"

"No, he won't."

"Who will, then—Frank?"

"You know he doesn't have any money."

"Well, I certainly don't, either. If I did, I'd buy a new harness—I've done about all the mending I can do."

John Woolworth sighed. His wife felt guilty, but she had promised Frank he would have his chance. She had promised Miss Penniman, too.

"I have a little money put aside," she said. "About fifteen dollars."

"Fifteen dollars!" her husband said. "Just from selling your fancy butter?"

Fanny Woolworth didn't answer that. Her brother Albon had given her a present of a little money now and then, and she had saved every cent of it. She did have some cash from selling butter, too, so John Woolworth wasn't all wrong about that.

"Well, I can't stop you from throwing it away," John Woolworth said. "Only remember one thing—I need Frank full time on the farm!"

The next day, Fanny Woolworth told Frank of her talk with his father. Frank, in turn, told Miss Penniman. "Then the Commercial College idea is no good," said the teacher sadly. "The classes are held only in the daytime."

Frank looked so downcast, Miss Penniman felt like crying. "I'm going to Watertown on

Saturday," she said. "Maybe I'll return with another idea. Don't give up hope!"

The Commercial College did have another idea for Miss Penniman to pass along to Frank. One of the professors would give Frank private lessons in bookkeeping—four evenings a week for six weeks at fifty cents a lesson.

"That's twelve dollars altogether!" exclaimed Frank to his mother.

It was, indeed, a frightening amount of money. It would take nearly all of Fanny Woolworth's savings—and what a long time it would take her to save that much again!

"Everything's sky high in price," said Frank's mother bravely, and that was very true. The country was feeling the strain of the war years. Ordinary needs of life, like flour and salt and coarse cotton yard goods, cost twice what they were worth. "All the more reason for you to get what extra schooling you can!" she added.

"I'll pay back every cent!" Frank promised.

Frank's father still did not like the idea. However, since the boy worked hard from sunup until the evening chores were done, John Woolworth did let him take the horses and drive to Watertown four nights a week.

Frank was often so tired after his lesson with the professor that he slept all the way back to the farm. Luckily the horses needed no guiding to get back to their barn—and Frank woke up as soon as the wagon wheels bumped over the ruts at the farm gate.

Six weeks later, however, he had his reward. He received a stiff white paper with fancy printing on it. It said that Frank Winfield Woolworth was "certified proficient in double-entry bookkeeping" and it was signed by his professor.

Fanny Woolworth proudly found a frame for the certificate and hung it in the front parlor with all her other treasures.

John Woolworth saw it as the end of a lot of tom-foolery. "Now you can settle down to the business of farming," he told his son.

Frank knew he could not expect his mother to pave his way for him again. Once and for all, he had to tell his father that he did not want to be a farmer.

"I've tried to tell you that, Father, over the years," said Frank. "Remember, I talked about being a railroad man or a lumberman——"

John Woolworth snorted. "Didn't think you were serious. Didn't I tell you at the time you didn't have the build for either of 'em?"

"I don't need muscles to work in a store——"

John Woolworth looked as if Frank had slapped him. "In a store!" he said. "No Woolworth has *ever* been a shopkeeper!"

Albon McBrier said much the same thing when he heard of Frank's plans. "No McBrier has ever been a shopkeeper," he stormed. "If what you want is to get away from home, come work for me."

Frank shook his head. "If I have to be a farmer, I'll stay with Father, Uncle Albon."

That remark softened John Woolworth a little. "Go look for a store job," he said. "Get it out of your system."

Full of high hope, Frank drove to Carthage, a town of about fifteen hundred people only a few miles from Great Bend. There were several stores in Carthage. Frank started with the first one—a furniture shop—and asked for work.

The owner hardly let him finish his sentence. "Have any experience selling?" he demanded.

When Frank shook his head, the storekeeper looked very cross. "Then why come in here? There's not enough work to keep *me* busy, let alone dead weight like you'd be!"

His face fiery hot, Frank turned and left the furniture shop. In turn, he visited the drygoods store, the butcher shop, even the undertaker's parlor. The question was always the same— "Any experience?"

Finally there was no store left to try. Frank had to go home and admit he had failed.

John Woolworth was not mean enough to say, "I told you so." With a twinkle in his eyes, he turned the business end of the farm work over to Frank. "I'm sure things will go a lot better now," he said, "since I have a 'proficient book-keeper' in charge."

Frank smiled a little, though he didn't feel a bit happy at the prospect of having to stay on the farm. Fanny Woolworth gave him a feather-light kiss on the cheek, and he looked at her with eyes that were sad.

"I don't know when I can pay you back now," he said in a tone so low only she could hear.

"Don't worry about it," she answered softly.

He didn't forget, though, and he did worry.

He even "hired out" to neighbors in his spare time, so that he could start to make good on his debt. When he handed her the first money in repayment, she gave it back to him.

"Keep it," she said, "toward that store of your own you're going to have someday."

Frank tried to smile. "That would be one way to get experience—working for myself," he said.

During the next winter, when farm work was slack, Frank often walked into Great Bend and lingered around Daniel McNeil's General Store. It still looked much as it had when he had first gone there for penny candy. The big stove was still in the middle of the store, with chairs pulled up close to it. Now that the weather was cold, a group of old men often sat on those chairs, enjoying the warmth from the crackling fire within. They would greet Frank happily, asking him to join them. Sometimes he did, and then he would play a game of checkers with one of them or read a newspaper to another whose eyesight was failing.

Usually, though, Frank wandered about the store, watching Daniel McNeil and taking note of what was stacked on the shelves and hung on the walls. Often Mr. McNeil asked Frank to get him something.

"You're taller'n I am, Frank," he'd say. "Reach me down that muskrat trap, will you?" Or "Weigh up a pound of crackers for Mrs. Allen, would you, boy?" or some other such request.

Frank was always so glad to help out, Daniel McNeil couldn't help noticing the quick way he did what he was asked. So, one day when he and Frank were alone in the store for a few moments, Mr. McNeil spoke his mind. "Frank," he said, "how would you like to help me out on rush days?"

Frank's eyes lighted up. "You know I'd like it!" he said.

"Trouble is, I can't afford to pay you any wages. However, if you'd like to do it for the experience——"

Frank's ears still burned from the memory of the refusals he had received in Carthage. Experience was as important as a "proficiency certificate." He knew that now.

"I *would* like to do it, Mr. McNeil!" he said, and they shook hands to settle the deal.

# Working for Nothing

DURING THE next few years, Frank continued to work on the farm, but he felt really alive only when he was helping out in the General Store. Since Daniel McNeil could not pay him, though, his father was not pleased with the deal Frank had made. He did not think the experience Frank was getting was worth the time the boy put in. However, since he had no real reason for making Frank stop, John Woolworth had to content himself with merely grumbling about the matter.

In March, 1873, though, Albon McBrier provided him with a reason. He offered Frank eighteen dollars a month plus food and a room to sleep in, if Frank would come work for him.

John Woolworth called a family meeting to discuss the offer. He held it in the parlor, where there should be nothing to take anybody's mind off the business at hand. He motioned Fanny Woolworth to one of the horsehair-stuffed seats beside the empty fireplace and took the other himself. Frank and Sum sat down on the stiff sofa facing their parents. The air of the seldom used room was chilly, and Frank shivered.

"You all know why we're here," John Woolworth said. "Albon has offered Frank a job on his farm. He is willing to pay generously, as is right when he's getting an experienced farmer."

Sum shot an amused glance at his brother.

John Woolworth, seeing Sum's smile, quickly added a remark to make Sum sorry. "It's a true test of worth, when a man does his best when his heart's not in it."

114

Frank, who was always quick to blush, felt the blood rush hotly into his cheeks. Sum, clearly not feeling sorry at all, muttered, " 'The world is your cow, but you have to do the milking'!"

"There are many upstate proverbs that apply in this case," John Woolworth said, "and you'd do well to heed some of those others yourself, Charles Sumner."

Fanny Woolworth coughed gently. Her husband, thus reminded of the reason they were gathered in the parlor, looked away from Sum and at Frank instead. "I didn't say anything, long as there was no use, but now I've got to speak up," he said. "You are twenty-one years old, Frank. You haven't any business working free for anyone, not even me, if cash money is offered you someplace else."

Frank felt his heart begin to beat rapidly. He swallowed, trying to calm himself. "You've needed me, Father," he said.

"So has Daniel McNeil," John Woolworth answered, "and both of us have been lucky to have you. Now you've got the chance to start shifting for yourself. You'd better take it."

Frank could not think of a thing to say. His father's last words echoed and re-echoed in his mind. He felt if he spoke, those would be the words he'd say, too, and he couldn't bring himself to do it.

"Sum'll be seventeen his next birthday," John Woolworth continued, when Frank remained silent. "He's through school—and I haven't heard any nonsense from him about not wanting to be a farmer. He can take your place on the farm. Yes, you'd better hire out to Albon."

Fanny Woolworth gasped. The words "hire out" had sounded unpleasantly in her ears. She had been brought up on the McBrier farm, after all, and she knew how hard her brother worked his hired men.

116

"I don't think Frank's strong enough to work for Albon," she said.

His mother's statement gave Frank the opening he needed. "If Uncle Albon's ready to pay me," he said, "maybe other people will be, too. Can't I just ask Mr. McNeil, Father?"

Once again John Woolworth gave in to his wife and his son. "Oh, all right," he said, getting up from his chair, "but this time I want results. I'll give you just two weeks to show them to me."

He strode out of the room, followed by Sum, leaving Frank and his mother alone. Fanny Woolworth's eyes filled with tears when Frank put his arms around her and hugged her.

"Go see Daniel McNeil," she said, her hands feeling his shoulder blades through his rough farm shirt, "and God go with you, son."

Frank went to see the storekeeper and explained his problem.

"I still can't pay you," Daniel McNeil said,

117

"but I'll keep my eyes and ears open, whenever I go to Watertown."

Frank kept the store when its owner went off to the bigger town. For some time the storekeeper's eyes and ears saw or heard nothing helpful for Frank. Then one day they did.

"There's a job open at Augsbury and Moore's!" Daniel McNeil said the minute he stepped back into his store. "Augsbury's a friend of mine. I'll give you a letter to take to him."

Augsbury and Moore's was the Corner Store where Frank and Sum had been so shabbily treated when they were little boys. Still, it was the best store in Watertown. If he could get a job there, Frank knew he would really have something to tell his father!

Frank drove to Watertown early the next day. He was ready to enter the store the moment it opened. As he went through the door, he was aware of the same things he had noticed years

118

ago—the soft murmur of voices and the scent of flowers. When a woman came out from behind a counter and spoke to him, he felt like turning around and running, but he stood his ground.

"I'm looking for Mr. Augsbury," he said in answer to her question about what he wanted. "I have a letter for him."

The woman put out her hand. "I'll take it," she said.

Frank shook his head. "I am to give it to him personally."

The woman shrugged. "You'll have to go to his house, then. He's at home, sick."

Frank's eyes flashed. "If you'll give me his address, that's what I'll do!" he said.

A young man gave Frank the directions he needed, and Frank turned and left the store gladly. As he had done years ago, he drew in great gulps of fresh, cold air the minute he was outside the hot store. His feet in their heavy boots

crunched on the hard-packed snow as he walked toward Mr. Augsbury's house.

A maid in a black dress with a starched white cap and a stiff white apron opened the door for him. Frank managed to tell her that he wanted to see Mr. Augsbury, so she walked ahead of him to one of the front rooms.

"A person to see you, sir," she said very properly, but she gave Frank a scornful look.

Mr. Augsbury was sitting in an armchair drawn up close to the fireplace. He had a woolen shawl over his knees in spite of the fact that a wood fire was blazing only a few inches from him. He looked up as Frank went toward him. "Hello, bub. What do you want—a job?"

Frank could hardly breathe. The room was hot, and the air was filled with the mixed smells of medicines. Besides that, he was very excited and his heart was pounding. "H-how did you g-guess?" he said, his words uncertain.

"I couldn't imagine why else anybody'd come to see a sick old man," Mr. Augsbury said, looking Frank up and down. "It's easy to see you are not a town boy."

Frank was wearing his only clothes—a stocking cap, rough shirt, thick cowhide boots, and heavy wool scarf in place of an overcoat—so he knew how he looked to Mr. Augsbury.

"Take off your scarf, bub," Mr. Augsbury said kindly. "Else you'll freeze when you go out."

Frank unwound the scarf. He pulled off his stocking cap, too.

"Now, then," Mr. Augsbury said, "what makes you think a job's open? Times are tight."

Frank pulled Daniel McNeil's letter out of his pocket. "Mr. McNeil told me so," he said. "He gave me this to give to you."

Mr. Augsbury pinched a pair of glasses onto his nose and read the letter. Then he folded it and placed it on his lap.

"Do you drink? Do you smoke? What do you do that's bad?" he asked Frank.

"I don't drink. I don't smoke. I go to church every Sunday," Frank said, "and sometimes I go twice. I don't think I do anything very bad— unless you think playing the flute is bad, that is."

"Not if you don't play it *badly*," Mr. Augsbury said, and he smiled.

Encouraged by the smile, Frank smiled back. He pushed back a lock of straight, blond hair and held his thin body very straight.

Mr. Augsbury picked up Daniel McNeil's letter again and waved it like a fan in front of his face. "Daniel says you're willing and a hard worker," he said, "but just 'cause you've helped him out now and then doesn't mean you're not green as grass. Anybody can weigh up a penny's worth of cheese—it's an *art* to sell behind the counter in *my* store."

Frank's shoulders sagged. He picked up his

scarf and started to wind it around his neck again. He ought not to have dreamed he could get a job with Augsbury and Moore!

"Hold on a minute, bub," Mr. Augsbury said. "You're green, all right, but I'm going to send you down to see Will Moore, anyway. If he wants to give you a trial, it's all right with me."

He wrote a few words on the bottom of Daniel McNeil's letter and handed it to Frank.

Frank felt very different when he walked into the Corner Store with Mr. Augsbury's note in his pocket. He had passed inspection by the senior partner—why should he be afraid of the junior partner?

When he saw William H. Moore, though, he knew why. Mr. Augsbury was a sick old man. Mr. Moore was only a dozen years older than Frank himself, but as elegant a figure as the hero in a picture book. He had neatly trimmed side whiskers and wore a full-skirted morning

coat with a silk collar. Sitting behind his slant-topped desk on a raised platform, he looked much more frightening than Mr. Augsbury had with a homely shawl over his knees.

Like Mr. Augsbury, Mr. Moore had questions for Frank, too.

"Why do you want to leave the farm? You don't think store hours are shorter, perhaps?"

"No, sir. I just want to work in a store. I don't like farming. I do like storekeeping."

"Storekeeping!" said William Moore coldly. "You don't know what storekeeping is."

Frank felt that Mr. Moore's words belittled his friend, Daniel McNeil. "Mr. McNeil keeps a good store," he said. "The folks in Great Bend couldn't get on without him."

William Moore's tone softened, as if he approved of Frank's standing by his friend. "I just meant, you don't know how to clerk in a store like this one. We'll take you on, though, if you're prepared to do all the dirty work."

"Wh-what do you mean?" asked Frank, hardly daring to believe that this elegant man was really offering him a job.

"I mean you'll have to get here earlier than anybody else to start the stoves going and sweep the floor. We'll expect you to wash windows, deliver packages, and do any odd jobs that need

126

to be done. It will be the hardest work you ever did in your life. Still think you'd rather work here than stay on that nice, clean farm?"

"Yes, sir," said Frank.

"If you pay attention, you'll learn a lot about how a real store is kept," Mr. Moore added, as if to soften the harsh picture he had drawn of the job he was offering Frank.

"Yes, sir," said Frank again. "What will you pay me, sir?"

William Moore looked shocked. "Pay you!" he said. "Why, you ought to pay *us* for hiring you!"

Frank felt as though Mr. Moore had hit him. "How long would I have to work for nothing?"

"It'll be at least six months before you're worth anything to us," Mr. Moore told him.

Frank thought fast. He had some money saved up, since his mother had made him keep all he'd earned at odd jobs. On it, he could live in Watertown for perhaps three months——

"I'll work the first three months for nothing," he said, "if you'll pay me three dollars and a half a week for the second three."

William Moore laughed. "Oh, all right," he agreed. "Report to work next Monday. The train will get you here in plenty of time."

"I'll be here!" said Frank, and drove home to break the news to his family.

# Corner Store
# Beginning

ON THE following Monday, the whole Woolworth family was up long before dawn. John Woolworth had to deliver a load of potatoes to town, so he could take Frank along. That way, Frank could save the train fare. Fanny Woolworth wanted to make sure Frank ate a hearty breakfast before he left home for good.

"Goodness knows whether you'll eat properly," she said, putting a heaping plateful of smoked pork and pan-fried potatoes in front of him, "once you don't have me to coax you!"

Frank was too excited to be hungry, but he knew his mother would worry if he didn't eat.

Filling his mouth with the crisp potatoes, he gazed around the familiar farm kitchen as if he would never see it again. He saw his mother's hickory-wood rocking chair, in which she sat to knit and to mend. He read once again the words of the sampler that hung on the wall above the woodstove—"A stitch in time saves nine." He saw every detail of the "washing corner"— the cake of yellow soap, dented tin wash-basin, roller towel, even the all-purpose comb on the shelf below the cloudy looking glass.

"Eat up, Frank," said his father. "It's late."

It was still dark when Frank tossed his bundle of clothing on top of the bags of potatoes and climbed up into the sleigh beside his father. He leaned down to take his flute out of his mother's hands. There were tears in Fanny Woolworth's eyes, but they remained unshed as long as Frank was looking at her. Sum stood beside her, holding a lantern in his hand.

John Woolworth took up the reins, and the horses moved off. Frank looked back over his shoulder. As long as the sleigh was within shouting distance, he heard his mother and Sum calling, "Good-by, Frankie!" and after that he saw the glow of Sum's swinging lantern.

When he could no longer see that, though, Frank turned to face the road ahead.

They drove through Great Bend just as the town was waking. At the General Store, Dan McNeil was watching for them. He ran out, apron and all, to hand Frank a farewell present. It was in a red-and-white-striped bag, so Frank knew it must be penny candy.

"Five cents' worth," said Daniel McNeil, and Frank knew the storekeeper, like himself, was remembering the first time they had met.

"He'd better give you the nickel," said John Woolworth, but Frank felt that what Daniel McNeil had given him was worth much more.

The snow was heavy on the road to Watertown, and it was the middle of the morning before John Woolworth stopped the team at the Courthouse railing. Frank was very upset, knowing he would be late for work. He jumped down from the sleigh and ran across the Public Square, arriving breathless at the Corner Store.

The first person he saw when he entered was Mr. Augsbury himself. Frank snatched off his cap before his employer greeted him.

"You're late, bub," the old man said. "The train got here on time. Where were you?"

"My father had to come to town with a load of potatoes," Frank said. "By riding with him, I saved the thirty-three cents' railroad fare, sir."

"You'll be living in town from now on, of course. Don't be late again."

"No, sir," said Frank.

Mr. Augsbury was not through. "Bub, don't they wear collars out your way?"

133

"No."

"No neckties, either?"

"No."

"Is this old flannel shirt the best you have?"

"Yes, sir."

"Well, you go to the men's wear department. Tell them I said to give you a white shirt, a collar, and a tie."

"I haven't the money to pay for them, sir."

"We'll take the cost out of your wages."

"But——"

"Later on," said Mr. Augsbury. "Now, go."

Frank went, getting the clothes he had been ordered to wear. By the time he was properly fitted out and ready to work again, Mr. Augsbury had gone to dinner. Mr. Moore was busy at his desk at the back of the store and paid no attention to Frank at all. Nobody else said a word to him either. The clerks stole glances at him and whispered to each other, but not one of them gave him a job to do. Frank just stood there, wishing he were back in Daniel McNeil's store, even if the only thing he could do there was play checkers with an old man.

Soon everybody had gone to dinner but Mr. Moore, and Frank was alone in the selling end of the store. Feeling very daring, he went behind one of the counters and tried to find out what kind of items were sold there. While he was bending down to see what was on the shelves beneath the counter, the front door opened and a customer came in. Frank heard the footsteps and stood up so fast he cracked his head on an open drawer.

The customer banged his fist on the counter. "Going to wait on me, young man?"

Frank's head hurt so he could scarcely speak, but he did manage to say, "S-sure!"

"Then, here's a list of what the wife wants."

Frank took the list, but he didn't know what

to do next. Unlike Daniel McNeil's store, few things were in plain sight here. Except for special display items, such as a single lace collar or a box of fancy soap, everything was in drawers or behind closed doors.

"I'm waiting, young man," said the customer.

Wildly Frank started pulling out drawers and opening cupboards. Luckily most of the things on the list were common goods like pins and thread, so Frank found them.

"How much?" asked the customer.

Frank looked at the price tags. The numbers on them didn't make sense to him. "I don't know," he said. "I'll have to ask Mr. Moore."

He almost tripped over his big feet as he hurried to the back of the store. "I-I can't read the p-price tags, sir," he said nervously.

Mr. Moore looked up. "Of course you can't. They're in code. We can't have just anybody able to find out how much we charge for things."

"B-but I've got a customer," said Frank.

"Shouldn't have. Who said you could?"

"I was the only one there," said Frank, trying to excuse himself.

William Moore's eyes flashed, and he got up. "That won't happen again. I'll wait on the customer myself. You watch."

Frank watched that day and for many days thereafter, whenever he had time off from his chores. That time didn't come very often, though. The store opened at seven o'clock, but Frank had to be on hand at six to start the fires, sweep, carry out ashes, fill the oil lamps, and polish the door handles.

Luckily he had found a boardinghouse he could afford quite close by. His landlady was a widow, her husband having died in the War, and she was happy to have young men like Frank living in her home.

Frank never did get to be a good salesman,

though. Store policy was for a clerk to press a customer to buy, even if the item was too expensive for his pocketbook. Frank just could not do it. He knew too well how hard money was to come by.

At the end of three months, however, he did start to get his three dollars and a half a week. He was a poor salesman, but he was a "crackerjack" at keeping the store clean and the stockroom in order. He learned to know the names and grades of all kinds of goods, and he soon knew what sold and what did not and why.

One afternoon, William Moore found Frank in the stock room, running a piece of red silk through his fingers.

"Nice stuff, isn't it?" he said to Frank.

"The color of the draperies in the cup-and-saucer house," said Frank, thinking of the room Joseph Bonaparte had fixed up for Napoleon.

"I wouldn't know about that," said William

138

Moore. "I do know there's something you can do besides run silk through your fingers."

"Yes, sir?"

"Wash the front window," Moore said. "I don't suppose I have to tell you to empty it first."

"No, sir," said Frank.

"And when you're through—retrim it."

"Yes, sir!"

At last Frank had a real chance to do something. He pulled down the shade to hide his actions from the town. Then he set busily to work, scrubbing the window display case until it was as clean as his mother's kitchen table. He didn't want to take any chances of soiling the beautiful things he planned to use to trim it.

When the store closed at nine o'clock, Frank was busy in the stock room. Mr. Moore, the last one to leave, looked at the window on his way out the door. It was still almost empty. One pair of ladies' black shoes was all it contained.

He turned, frowning, to Frank, who was coming toward him with a gray shawl in his hands. "Don't make this store a joke, Woolworth, or you'll be sorry." Not waiting for Frank to reply, he left, closing the door firmly behind him.

Frank worked until long after midnight. He used every shade of red cloth he could find, from cherry-red to plum-rose, having the cloth spilling from the bolts like water over the dam in the river at the end of the street. At their base, as at the bottom of the waterfall, he set the stock items that would show up best against the red background. He tried one thing after another, until he thought he had exactly the right ones. Only then did he put out the lights, pull up the shade, and go home.

The next morning when William Moore came to work, he found a group of ladies standing in front of his show window, oh-ing and ah-ing about Frank's arrangement.

140

"Look at those *sweet* little black boots!" one of them exclaimed.

"That *lovely* shawl—it looks as if it were made of cobwebs!" said another.

"The colors!" said a third. "Whoever would have *dreamed* you could mix those shades of red and have them look so marvelous!"

Mr. Moore took one long look at his own window. "Who, indeed?" he said to himself.

It was not his custom to say anything when he was pleased. This time was no exception. From that day on, however, Frank was expected to dress all the windows. His salary was raised to four and a half dollars, so he knew he had found favor with William Moore.

The trouble was, he was expected to do all the janitor work as usual, too. That, to Frank, did not seem fair, but he didn't yet know what to do about it.

# Ups and Downs

FRANK WAS proud of the attention his window dressing got from the townspeople. He was prouder still of the way he had risen in the eyes of his fellow clerks. They didn't think of him as a "country hayseed" any longer, that was sure!

Then, when he had been with Augsbury and Moore for two and a half years, he found six dollars instead of four and a half in his weekly pay envelope. That was a whole dollar for each working day!

"Why, I'm rich!" cried Frank.

To prove it, he went on a clothes-buying spree. He bought a woolen overcoat with a velvet collar and a high silk hat. He wore the fine outfit to church on Easter Sunday, when he took his new girl there for the first time.

The girl was Jennie Creighton, a young dress-maker who had recently come from Canada to live with a cousin in Watertown. Frank's land-lady had introduced him to her.

"Play one of your Irish tunes for her, Frank, my boy," the widow had said, "but not one of the sad ones. She's homesick enough as it is, poor little thing!"

The young people soon found they had a good many interests in common besides music. Being a dressmaker, Jennie shared Frank's interest in fabrics and colors. She was, in fact, a good deal of help to him in his window dressing. She suggested ideas that Frank could never have thought of himself.

The result was, Frank began to think he would be happy to have Jennie by his side for life.

"She can't be married to a—a janitor, though,"
he stormed to himself. Fired with that thought
he at last dared to go to Mr. Augsbury and speak
his mind. "I've been doing enough work for
three men," he said firmly. "I've been stock
clerk as well as display man—and cleaning up
after everybody besides."

Mr. Augsbury waited until Frank had finished
his outburst. "You do look a mite pale and thin,"
he said kindly, "but you've come to the wrong
man to complain. I'm retiring from the firm,
Mr. Woolworth. You'll have to go to Will Moore
with your problem."

Frank didn't like that idea at all. William
Moore worked long hours himself, often not
even taking time out for dinner. Still, afraid Mr.
Augsbury would tell his partner of Frank's com-
plaint anyway, he decided he must talk to him.

"I'm often here until midnight, Mr. Moore,"
Frank said, ending his tale.

"You wouldn't be, if you didn't do a hundred displays before one pleases you," William Moore answered coldly. "This isn't New York City, you know. We're simple people here."

Frank knew it was no use. If he wanted to stay on at the Corner Store, he would just have to accept that as a fact.

Naturally his feelings were hurt, and he went to Jennie for sympathy.

"Never mind," she said, her blue eyes understanding the hurt pride in his. "When you have a store of your own, you can redo every window a thousand times, if you want to!"

Like his mother, Jennie spoke of "a store of your own" just as if she were sure he'd have one someday. Frank wasn't as sure of that as they were, but he *was* surer than ever that he had to have Jennie for his wife. *When* would he be able to support her?

Another dry-goods store in Watertown now

was owned by A. Bushnell. It was the Corner Store's rival in many ways, but not, Frank could say proudly, when it came to window displays. *They* were terrible!

In the fall of 1875, Golding, the head clerk at Bushnell's, left that store to open one of his own in Michigan. He had scarcely left town before Frank went to apply for Golding's job.

As he walked through the store on the way to Bushnell's office, he looked at the messy counters and his hands fairly itched to beautify them.

"What weekly salary do you want?" Mr. Bushnell asked him, delighted to snatch William Moore's prize away from the Corner Store.

Thinking how much good he could do the store, Frank decided to aim high. "I think I am worth ten dollars," he said.

Bushnell nodded. "That will be all right."

Hardly daring to believe his ears, Frank shook hands with Mr. Bushnell. Then, feeling as if he were walking on air, he returned to tell William Moore of his action.

William Moore had a new partner, Mr. Perry R. Smith. Frank had to face the two young men together.

"Of course," Frank said, almost hopefully, "if you care to meet the salary, I'll stay here."

He soon realized that Mr. Moore and Mr. Smith had discussed him before, because it was Perry Smith who answered.

"You're not worth it," he said, "and Bushnell will soon find that out. You're a perfect bust as a salesman—and selling's the job he's hiring you to do."

Perry Smith's words were harsh, but Frank was so pleased with himself they didn't hurt him as they might have another time. During his dinner hour, he rushed to Jennie with his news. She, of course, made him feel he was the smartest man in the whole world.

"I've been living like a king on six dollars a week," Frank said. "Making ten dollars, I can save four easily. When I've a nest egg, will you marry me, Jennie?"

"Oh, I will!" said Jennie.

Next week Frank went to work at Bushnell's.

"You won't mind sleeping in the basement, will you?" was the first thing Mr. Bushnell said to him. "I'll give you a gun, and the check boy, Harry Moody, for company. The two of you together ought to be able to protect this place from burglars."

Frank didn't like the idea, but it would mean he could save the three dollars and a half he paid his landlady each week. That, in turn, would mean he and Jennie could get married that much sooner.

Living in the dark, damp basement was not good for Frank, who was already far too pale and thin. Rooming on Franklin Street, he had at least had some fresh air on the walk to and from work. Now Mr. Bushnell expected him to be on hand twenty-four hours a day.

Perry Smith had been right about something else Mr. Bushnell expected. He had thought he was hiring a salesman—and he didn't care what else Frank could do if he couldn't sell.

"I don't *want* my windows dressed up," he said, "and I like the counters the way they are."

Frank tried his best to do the job for which he'd been hired, but his heart was not in it. If it weren't for that lovely ten-dollar bill every week, he would wish he had never heard of A. Bushnell's store.

One day there wasn't a ten-dollar bill in his pay envelope. There were eight dollars instead.

"Hasn't there been some mistake?" Frank asked Mr. Bushnell.

"No," said the merchant bluntly. "I have clerks better than you who are getting only six dollars a week. You can be glad I don't cut you back to that."

There was nothing Frank could do but accept the cut. He worked harder than ever, trying to sell, but even his looks worked against him. He was so white and pale-lipped that people didn't want him to wait on them.

Then, one morning just before Christmas, his roommate Harry awoke to hear Frank talking wildly and burning up with fever.

Frank had pneumonia, and he must have complete rest and constant nursing if he was ever to get well. John and Fanny Woolworth came for their son and took him back to the farm to nurse him back to health.

Through the winter Frank lay in bed. He recovered from the pneumonia, because his mother and Jennie took turns nursing him, but he felt very, very weak.

"I'm a failure," he kept saying over and over.

"Whatever made me think I could ever have a store of my own?"

"I encouraged you to think so," Fanny Woolworth said. "I thought storekeeping was an easier job than farming. Now I'd say it was a great deal harder."

By March, Frank was up and around again. He wasn't strong enough yet to do a man's chores, but he could lend his mother a hand now and then. He could carry a pail of snow to the wood stove for her, so she could melt it and use the water for washing clothes. He could wring the heavy clothes out for her, too, and hang them on the line. He even enjoyed bringing them in again, dry and stiff. They smelled so clean when the cold air from them met the warmth of the kitchen!

Jennie caught him once, burying his nose in one of the bed sheets. She laughed.

He caught her hand in his. "Would you be

a farmer's wife?" he asked. "Would you, Jennie, would you?"

She patted his cheek, rosy now with the fresh country air. "I'd planned to be a merchant's wife," she said, "but I could change my plans."

On June 11, 1876, they were married in the parlor of the Woolworth house. They had no money at all, but the bank in Watertown was willing to lend them some. Frank found a four-acre farm that would be just right for raising chickens, so they bought it and moved in.

As a wedding present, John Woolworth gave them some of his chickens to start with. They hoped to make a living from the first by selling eggs. Later, after their flock had grown bigger, they could sell chickens, too.

For four months they struggled along. They found they had to eat both chickens and eggs to keep life in their bodies.

"Oh," said Frank finally, after a procession of

stewed chicken dinners, "I wish I never had to see another chicken or taste another chicken or smell another chicken as long as I live."

That same day a letter arrived from William Moore. Would Frank stop by, next time he found himself in Watertown?

"I wonder what he wants," mused Frank, reading the letter aloud to Jennie.

"Why don't you go in and see?"

"Today?" asked Frank eagerly.

Jennie shook her head. "You don't want to seem too curious," she said, "even though I can see you are."

Frank waited a few days, but then he could stand it no longer. He packed some eggs in a basket so he'd have an excuse for going. Then he set off for Watertown.

"Remember, don't seem too eager!" Jennie called after him.

He was, though. He went straightway to the

154

Corner Store, with the basket of eggs held tightly in his hands.

William Moore got up to greet him. Only then did Frank realize what he was carrying.

"Here!" he said, handing Mr. Moore the basket. "Some strictly fresh eggs for you!"

"Why—er—thank you!" said William Moore, looking around for a place to put the gift. Finally setting it in a corner, he motioned Frank to a chair. "Sit down, Frank, do."

Somewhat amazed, Frank did so. Mr. Moore had called him "Frank," too. What had brought about the change?

"I won't beat about the bush, Frank," William Moore said. "Business hasn't been so good since you left. Dressing up the windows again would help. Will you come back and do it for us—at ten dollars a week?"

Frank was tempted to say yes at once, but he knew he couldn't. He had a wife and a farm to think about—in addition to all those hated chickens.

"I'll have to consult my wife," he said.

Back he went to the farm once more.

Jennie had an instant answer to the problem of what to do. "Frank," she said, "you go back to the store. Live in the old boardinghouse. I'll stay here and take care of the chickens until we get a chance to sell them."

The following Monday, Frank was back in the Corner Store. He went home every other week end for a whole year. Then a neighbor offered to trade her sewing machine for the chickens.

Since Jennie had always wanted a sewing machine, they agreed to the swap. Then they rented the farm and moved into Watertown.

By Christmas, 1877, the Frank Woolworths were happily at home in a wing of a two-story frame house on Franklin Street in Watertown.

# The Five-cent Table

FOR A WHILE after Frank's return, business was better at the Corner Store. In late spring, though, trade started dropping off again. Moore and Smith had to dismiss several of their clerks and cut the salaries of all the others. Frank's pay was now only eight and a half dollars instead of ten dollars a week.

One day when there were no customers at all in the store, a young man walked in. Frank was sure he had seen him before, but who was he? He was very well dressed, so William Moore himself went to wait on him.

The young man smiled broadly and put out his

hand. "Remember me?" he asked. "Golding, formerly of A. Bushnell's?"

"Of course," said William Moore. "Set up for yourself someplace in Michigan, didn't you? You took one of my top men with you, too. How is Barrett, anyway?"

"Fine," said Golding. He looked around the store. "How's business, Mr. Moore?"

"As you can see, it's slow. Never knew it to be worse, in fact."

"Too bad," said Golding. "Maybe you aren't keeping up with the times, Mr. Moore."

Frank, who was listening to every word the two men said, held his breath. What would Mr. Moore say to *that?*

"Oh," William Moore answered, "I wouldn't say that, Mr. Golding. I make twice-yearly trips to New York City, just to be sure I learn about what's new."

"Ever try a table of 'come-on' items?" Golding

went on. "You know—offer things at cheap prices, just to get people to come into your store?"

"Never," said William Moore. "You know the kind of place we run here. We're known for carrying only top-grade stock."

Once again Golding looked around the store. Uneasily Frank did, too, trying to see it as Golding would. There weren't any customers buying top-grade goods, that was certain.

"Why don't you try a five-cent table?" Golding said boldly. "Barrett and I often do. In fact, I'm on my way to New York to order the special stock now. Spellman Brothers makes a whole line of five-cent stuff."

Golding's idea made sense to Frank. He wondered what items could be sold for five cents. It would be exciting to fix up a whole tableful.

William Moore, though, did not seem much interested. "I might try your idea sometime," he said, but he didn't sound as if he ever would.

Golding shrugged his shoulders. "Just remember the name," he said, and turned to leave. "Spellman Brothers, New York City."

William Moore never said a word to Frank about his talk with Golding. Frank, naturally, never said anything either, but he couldn't seem to get the five-cent-table idea out of his mind.

In late August, William Moore went on his usual buying trip to New York City. When he returned, he made a special point of seeking Frank. "I know you were listening that day Bushnell's former clerk was in here," he said. "What did you think of this special sale idea?"

Frank's face lighted up. "I thought it made sense, Mr. Moore," he said.

William Moore nodded. "Well, I bought a hundred dollars' worth of five-cent goods the other day. When they arrive, you'll be in charge of them. You make all the plans—I don't want to have anything to do with them."

Now Frank felt really excited. This was the kind of chance he'd been dreaming of! He could hardly wait until the shipment arrived.

The goods came a week before the County Fair. Frank felt that was a good sign. At Fair time, people were all in good spirits. They had a little money in their pockets and planned to spend it. The five-cent sale must begin the day the Fair opened!

The night before opening day, Frank never left the store. He had decided not to "dress up" the show window at all. Instead, he made a large sign. In foot-high red letters it said:

HUGE FIVE-CENT SALE

That was the only thing in the display.

For the sale counter, Frank pushed two long tables together. He placed them where they would be seen the minute anybody entered the store. He covered them with bright red cloths that hung down to the floor all the way around. Then he set out the five-cent goods.

He kept each kind of item apart from every other kind, but put things that might sell together side by side. Baby bibs and safety pins were close, and quite apart from tin pans and water dippers. Writing paper, steel pens, and pencils were near book straps. Combs and soap were together, as were needles, thimbles, and thread.

On his way into the store the next morning, William Moore stopped to look at Frank's display. He watched Frank put up a sign that said:

ANY ARTICLE ON THIS COUNTER
FIVE CENTS

"I never thought I'd stoop to this to get customers," he said, and his tone of voice sounded as if he were touching something unclean.

162

Just before seven o'clock, Frank propped open the outside door. He stepped outside, expecting to see people eagerly reading the sign in the show window. There was no one near the store at all.

From the fairground at the end of the street he could hear the calliope, or steam piano. It was playing "Listen To the Mocking Bird," and sounded like a flock of whistles all going at once. There were crowds of people in town, all right, but they were all heading for the Fair.

Frank felt a little sick. Maybe he had picked the worst possible time to have the sale. Maybe no one would ever know the Corner Store was lowering its standards and was out to get any customer who had a nickel in his pocket or purse.

Along about midmorning, a woman came hurrying in. She had a sack of peanuts in her hand and her mouth was full of them too. "Need a pin," she mumbled to Frank. "Tore my dress. Got anything like that in this fancy store?"

163

"Yes, indeed," said Frank, and waved his hand toward the special table. He watched the look on her face change when she saw the sign:

ANY ARTICLE ON THIS COUNTER
FIVE CENTS

"Is this *Moore's*?" she cried, speaking clearly, now that she had swallowed the peanuts.

"Yes, ma'am," said Frank.

The woman's surprise made him think back to the time he and Sum had first come into the Corner Store. He even remembered that he had said to Sum, "There ought to be a store where nobody bothers you. Where you can walk up and down 'til you see something you want——"

"I'm Frank Woolworth, at your service," he said now. "I'll be just across the aisle."

He took out a drawer full of sewing silks and pretended to be counting them. Really he was

watching the customer very closely. He saw her pick up a packet of pins and set it to one side. Then she moved on eagerly, looking at everything and every once in a while adding an item to the pile of goods she was setting aside. At last Frank saw her take a deep breath and open her purse. She counted the coins in it and then counted the things she wanted to buy.

"Young man!" she called.

Frank hurried to her.

"I want all of these things," she said. "You can put the pins and the buttonhook and the knitting needles in the tin pan and wrap 'em altogether. The watch key can go in it, too."

Frank put all the little items into the pan and then wrapped it in coarse paper and tied the bundle with string. Leaving a loop for a handle, he gave it to her with a big smile.

Taking it, she laughed excitedly. "Wait till I tell 'em what-all I got for twenty-five cents!"

The "rest of 'em" seemed to be everybody for miles around. The news of the great sale at the "fancy Corner Store" was more exciting than whose cake had won the blue ribbon. Many of the people who came bought regular goods at regular prices as well as the five-cent things they had come to buy. By nightfall all the clerks were ready to drop with fatigue, and the five-cent table was completely bare.

"I'd never have believed it!" cried William Moore when Frank brought him the news. "I'll send a telegram to Spellman Brothers and tell them to rush a new shipment by tonight's train!"

The story was the same every day during Fair week. When William Moore added up the profits, he was delighted. "Well, Frank," he said, "you did a fine job. It's over now, though. Back to business as usual."

"But, sir—" began Frank.

William Moore stopped him. "I know what

you want to say, but don't bother. We'll run a special sale like this twice a year or so—but the people won't want it all the time. Not our regular customers, anyway."

Frank thought of the second day of the sale, when "regular customers" shoved visiting farmers' wives aside to get to the five-cent tables. Maybe they wouldn't do that often—— "You're probably right sir," he said.

During the next few weeks, though, Frank's desire to have a store of his own grew. This time, though, it wasn't just *a* store that he wanted. It was a *Five Cent Store*. He was sure there was a need for one, not in Watertown but in a bigger town where there were more factories.

He talked about his idea to Jennie. Then he went to William Moore. "How much money would I have to have?" he asked.

"Oh—probably three hundred dollars," said Mr. Moore. "Can you raise it?"

168

"I'll try," said Frank, thinking perhaps his Uncle Albon would lend him the money.

Uncle Albon, though, would do no such thing. "I'd lend you money to buy a farm," he said, "but not for such nonsense as a five cent store!"

This, too, Frank reported to Jennie.

"Ask Mr. Moore to lend it to you," she said.

"If I did that, I'd have to put in every penny of our savings, too," he said. "How would we live from day to day?"

Jennie patted the sewing machine. "I'll do dressmaking again," she said.

Frank went back to William Moore.

"If you have enough money saved up to rent a store," the merchant told him, "Moore and Smith's will order three hundred dollars' worth of nickel goods and lend them to you."

On the last day of January, 1879, Frank set out for Utica, New York, with twenty-five dollars in cash in his pocket.

# The First Stores

FRANK TRAMPED up and down Genesee Street looking for empty stores. He found several, but the landlords all wanted more monthly rent, payable at once, than Frank had in his pocket. Finally he turned down Bleecker Street, where the stores were smaller. He saw a TO LET sign over the door of one of them, and the added note: "Anyone interested should knock on the door to the left."

Frank knocked. An old man answered.

"Are you the owner of the place next door?" Frank asked.

"Yep."

"May I have a look at it?"

"Guess so. Door's unlocked."

Frank walked in. The room was about thirteen feet wide on the street and twenty feet deep. It didn't look as if it had been used for a long time. It was cold and had a closed-in smell. The walls were mustard color and dirty, but there was good storage space and fairly good lighting. The place would do, if he could afford it.

Frank went back to see the owner. "What's the rent?" he asked.

"Thirty-five dollars a month *in advance*, and you'll have to sign a lease for a year."

Frank's face must have told his feelings, because the old man continued speaking. "What's the matter—don't you have that much?"

"Not with me," said Frank, "but what's really bothering me is having to sign a lease."

The owner was silent, studying Frank's face. "What *would* suit you?" he asked finally.

Thinking he had nothing to lose by speaking up, Frank said, "Renting from month to month—and not paying the *first* thirty-five dollars until the end of the first month."

The old man laughed a big, booming laugh. "Well, if you don't beat all!" he said. "I've a good mind to agree, blest if I haven't!"

Feeling braver still, Frank said, "Better a deal like that than an empty store!"

"Now there you've said a mouthful, young man," said the owner. "All right—done!" he added, handing a big key to Frank.

Frank's heart was pounding when he turned the key to lock *his store*. It was still beating double time when he boarded the train to go back to Watertown. At last! At last! it seemed to say in time to the clicking of the train wheels.

Back in Watertown, he rushed home to tell Jennie the news. Then he hurried to Moore and Smith's to see the stock of five-cent items William

Moore had ordered for him. He knew what goods he wanted to start off with—the same sort of things that had sold so well on that first five-cent table during Fair week.

In the stock room of Moore and Smith's, he helped the stock boy pack the goods and address the crates to Utica. Then he hurried back to his store to get it ready for them.

He scrubbed the place from top to bottom with hot water and pine-scented soap. He painted the walls a pleasant dove-gray. Then he bought plain pine boards and built counters and shelves, painting them a darker gray than the walls. In front of the counters he hung bright red cloth—the same sort of cloth he had used during Fair week. He felt that red was his lucky color.

Frank's in-pocket money was soon used up, because he had other expenses, too. He had two thousand handbills printed, announcing his grand opening, and he had to pay a small boy to push them under doors for him. Most important of all, he had a painter make a huge red-and-gold store front sign. It said: GREAT FIVE CENT STORE in letters a foot high.

When this sign was in place over the store, Frank stepped outside to admire it. It was as eye-catching as a circus wagon, and Frank hoped

it would draw many people who would become his customers.

The Grand Opening was set for eight o'clock the evening of February 22, 1879—but it wasn't very grand. When Frank counted up his "take" at midnight, he had a total of nine dollars. The people of Utica must have had more exciting things to do than to shop that Saturday night!

Monday's business was better, though, and two days later it was so good Frank had to hire a clerk to help him. On March 4 he sent Moore and Smith a hundred dollars in payment toward the three hundred they had loaned him. Eagerly he began to think that he would soon be able to have Jennie and their baby come to Utica to live with him.

Then, in early April, business fell off. People began to complain that there weren't enough different things they could buy for a nickel. Besides, they wanted something to compare with what they were buying. When everything cost five cents, there was no choice.

Frank struggled on through April and into May, but at last he had to admit to himself that the Utica store was a failure. Did that mean he himself was a failure, or did the truth lie somewhere else?

Alone in his Utica boardinghouse, he spent many a sleepless night asking himself questions. At last he believed he had found the honest answers. The fault was not with him or with his store idea. It was with Utica and the bad location he had picked for the store. What he had to do was find the right city and the right spot.

From a number of people, Frank had heard good things about the city of Lancaster, Pennsylvania. It was about the size of Utica, but it was peopled by the thrifty Pennsylvania Dutch, who knew value but wanted to save money whenever possible.

176

Leaving the Great Five Cent Store in charge of his clerk, Frank went to Lancaster to look over the place himself.

The next Sunday he went back to Watertown to tell Jennie about his trip.

"Right away I felt that Lancaster was the place for me!" he said eagerly. "There's an amazing air of business and prosperity there—and I found a store that will be perfect for my purpose in every way!"

Jennie looked a little worried at Frank's excitement. "How can you start another store?" she asked. "Will you have any money left after you pay all the bills you owe in Utica?"

"There's enough cash in the bank there to pay all those bills," Frank assured her.

"What about Moore and Smith?"

"Well, William Moore's a good businessman— and Perry Smith will go along with whatever Moore decides. I'm going to ask him to give me three hundred dollars *more* new goods to stock the Lancaster store!"

Frank's honest belief in himself and the new store found favor with William Moore. He gave Frank the new goods he asked for and wished him great good luck.

On June 11, Frank closed the store in Utica. Ten days later—June 21, 1879—he opened the new store in Lancaster. Centered above the door was the old, red-and-gold GREAT FIVE CENT STORE sign from the Utica store. At both sides of this sign there were new signs, also in red and gold. These signs read:

F. W. WOOLWORTH'S
FIVE AND TEN CENT STORE

Frank had taken the complaints of the Utica shoppers to heart. This time he would give his customers a choice of goods—those that cost five cents and those that cost ten.

The Lancaster store proved highly popular with the Pennsylvania Dutch housewives, and those thrifty women taught Frank a thing or two.

"Don't use that good brown wrapping paper for these things," one of them said to him, when he was wrapping up the pie plates and cake cutters she had bought. "Use newspapers."

"Where will I get enough newspapers, madam, to wrap all the things you good ladies buy?" he asked, smiling at his customer.

"From the newspaper office at two cents a pound," she told him.

Frank adopted her idea at once. He had been paying eight cents a pound for standard wrapping paper—just think of saving six cents a pound on the quantity he needed!

On Saturday nights Jennie often came to the store to help out. She brought year-old baby Helena with her, putting her to sleep in a packing box underneath the counter. Sometimes Helena would wake up and cry. Then the home-loving Lancaster wives and mothers would stop and ask to see her.

"We like a good family man," they told Jennie. "We like Mr. Woolworth and you both."

Then they would pat little Helena on the top of her head or pinch her rosy cheeks before they moved on hunting for bargains.

By the end of 1880, the Woolworths were so rich that Frank decided to take the first vacation of his life. Of course, he took his family with him. All dressed up in brand-new clothes, they went back to Watertown.

Frank had grown a thick mustache, but there was no mistaking him when he walked proudly across the Public Square with Jennie on his arm.

When they entered Moore and Smith's, William Moore came hurrying to greet them, holding out a hand to each of them. "Welcome! Welcome!" he cried, and Frank, looking about him, felt that this was *really* the greatest possible moment in his life. Certainly, it was an enormous contrast to the reception he had received on that November day so long ago!

From Moore and Smith's the Woolworths went to the livery stables, where they rented a fancy carriage and two lively black horses. They drove to the McBrier farm at Pillar Point, where Uncle Albon, too, was quick to welcome them.

"It's a proud day for the McBriers!" he said, reaching up to take baby Helena. "Doesn't seem so long ago since I was holding *you* this way, Frank, my boy."

Frank stepped down and gave his hand to Jennie. "I haven't forgotten, Uncle Albon," he said. "I don't forget much," he added, and this statement seemed to make his uncle feel quite uncomfortable.

"Yes—well—'er—you showed me, didn't you?" the older man admitted.

Frank's aunt appeared in the doorway. "What's keeping you?" she asked gaily. "Come on in where I can get my hands on that baby!"

They walked up the steps and into the house. As he entered, Frank took a deep breath.

"What smells so good, Aunt?" he asked.

She smiled at him. "You sound just like the little boy who used to come a-visiting," she said.

"Well?" teased Frank.

"It's everything you used to like best," she answered. "Nothing's too good for Frank Winfield Woolworth, is it?"

Frank was speechless with embarrassment. Jennie came to his rescue.

"He's Frank Winfield officially, Aunt," she said, "and the world knows him as F.W. To us, though—to you and me and all his family—he's just our Frank."

Aunt McBrier shook her head. "To me, he's Frankie," she said.

# Tower of Nickels and Dimes

FOLLOWING HIS success in Lancaster, Frank Woolworth opened branch stores just as fast as he could make the money necessary to equip them. He took in several partners, the first of them his brother Sumner. Not all of the new stores were successful. If they weren't, he closed them, just as he had the store in Utica. Sometimes his partners protested, but he always had the same answer for them.

"The Dutch farmers taught me to manage my own business," he said, "and never to let my business manage me. It was from them, too, that I learned to make the branch stores stand or fall

183

according to their own value. Every town has to support its own store. I shall never permit my system of stores to have to bear the burden of a single one."

Another policy he followed from the beginning. After he paid off Mr. Moore and Mr. Smith, he never borrowed money again. That, too, he learned from the wealthy Dutch farmers. They never went into debt and they always paid with cash. They bought at the lowest prices and they bought not a cent's worth more than they needed.

"Perhaps I would have made money faster," Frank Woolworth said, "if I had borrowed the money to equip my stores. I doubt it, though. I think that if I had done that, I would have been a failure instead."

All the Woolworth stores did business the same way. Their managers bought goods for cash and sold them for only slightly more than cost. Their selling methods were the same, too. A customer was allowed to walk up and down at will. He could pick up and examine any article. Only if he decided to buy it would a clerk appear.

"Goods," F.W. said often, "have to sell themselves. No salesman in any store of mine is going to breathe down the neck of any customer. I remember too well how I felt when someone did that to *me!*"

By the year 1910, Mr. F. W. Woolworth had gathered the nickels and dimes of the country together to create a personal fortune of fifty million dollars. He could buy himself anything in the world he wanted.

What he wanted most was to own the tallest building in the world. It would be the headquarters of the Woolworth Company and an enormous advertisement for the F. W. Woolworth stores. He wanted it to be so lofty and beautiful that people would come and admire it from afar.

Selecting the site for such a building was most important. It must be in the heart of New York City—that was all F.W. knew.

"I walked up and down Broadway," he said later, telling how he had found it, "and looked at people. I watched them as they turned into side streets. I saw where the traffic was thickest. After standing for half an hour watching the crowd turn from Broadway to Park Place, I knew that was where my Tower of Nickels and Dimes had to be."

Into this monument to the buying power of nickels and dimes F. W. Woolworth poured the enormous sum of thirteen and a half million dollars. He paid for the building of it as he always paid for goods—with cash.

Because the Woolworth Tower was to be so high, it had to be built on a foundation of solid bed rock. Bed rock was a hundred and twenty feet below the streets of New York, so it was a long time before the steel framework of the building could be seen above the sidewalk.

It began to show, though, on November 15, 1911. After that, from an office he had taken just across from the building site, Frank Woolworth watched it rise.

His many partners shook their heads over the whole deal. "You'll never find tenants for an office building that big," they said. "You'll find you've built yourself an empty monument, we fear—you'll be sitting there in lonely splendor."

F.W. chuckled at all of them. "Businessmen will fall over themselves to say their offices are in the tallest building on earth."

On July 1, 1912, the flag went up on top of the tower. This meant only that the steel framework was done, but ten months later the entire building was finished.

The Woolworth Tower was pure white, and its stonework looked almost like lace. In spite of

its size, it had a cathedral-like appearance. It was more beautiful than Frank's wildest dreams had ever imagined it could be.

The building was opened formally on the night of April 24, 1913, when Frank Woolworth held a banquet in the dining hall for his friends, business associates, and a large group of Congressmen from Washington, D.C.

By seven o'clock, the guests had all been seated. Thirty minutes later, the lights were put out and the crowd sat in darkness. There was a moment of silence, until President Woodrow Wilson, seated in the White House in Washington, pressed a button. Then, as if by magic, all the lights in the entire building were turned on, some eighty thousand of them. In the banquet hall a hidden orchestra broke into "The Star Spangled Banner." The diners rose to their feet, applauding their host.

"Gentlemen," called the toastmaster, "I give

you F. W. Woolworth, the Napoleon of Commerce!"

All the guests cheered wildly. Frank Woolworth, now a stout gentleman with a white mustache, wiped away a tear with his enormous white napkin.

"I call him 'Napoleon,' " the toastmaster went on, "because I know that Napoleon Bonaparte has long been the hero of F. W. Woolworth. Back when Frank was a poor farm boy, he read a life of that other poor boy who became Emperor of all the French. From it, he learned that *you can get what you want if you try hard enough*. Well, gentlemen, F.W. wanted the tallest building in the world—and he got it!"

After the toastmaster had seated himself, Frank Woolworth stood up. "Gentlemen," he said, "do you know what really made this building possible? I'll tell you. Over forty years ago, I went to work to learn the drygoods business in Watertown, New York. Mr. William Moore taught me my first lessons. Later he and his partner, Perry Smith, loaned me the money I needed to start out in business for myself. I could never have done it without their help. Those gentlemen are both here tonight. Mr. Moore and Mr. Smith, stand up!"

The two small-town merchants stood up and received thundering applause led by F. W. Woolworth himself. Then Frank continued.

"Without a good manager, I could never have started a second store. Therefore I want you all to meet my first branch-store manager—my brother, Charles Sumner Woolworth!"

Sum, too, received hearty applause, and so the evening proceeded with good feelings all around. When it was over, and the last guest had left, Frank turned to his brother.

"I've never been so tired in all my life," he said, "but, Sum—I've never been so happy!"

When F. W. Woolworth died in April, 1919, the newspapers wrote glowing words about him.

"He won a fortune," said the New York *Morning Sun*, "not in showing how little could be sold for how much, but how much could be sold for a little."

The New York *Evening World* had the final words: "Woolworth made his dreams come true by his grit and his faith in homely things and homely people."

A million people walk into Woolworth stores all over the world every day. The importance of dime stores to community life is so great, no shopping center is complete without one.

# More About This Book

## WHEN F. W. WOOLWORTH LIVED

1852    FRANK WINFIELD WOOLWORTH WAS BORN NEAR RODMAN, NEW YORK, APRIL 13.

There were thirty-one states in the Union.

Millard Fillmore was President.

The population of the country was about 24,840,000.

1858    THE WOOLWORTH FAMILY MOVED TO GREAT BEND, NEW YORK.

The Lincoln-Douglas debates were held, 1858.

The War between the States was fought, 1861-1865.

President Lincoln was assassinated, 1865.

1868    FRANK ATTENDED COMMERCIAL COLLEGE AT WATERTOWN, NEW YORK, FOR SIX WEEKS.

Louisa May Alcott wrote *Little Women*, 1869.

The first transcontinental railroad was completed, 1869.

Ulysses S. Grant was President, 1869-1877.

1873 FRANK BEGAN TO WORK AT AUGSBURY AND MOORE'S CORNER STORE AT WATERTOWN.

Alexander Bell invented the telephone, 1876.

Bicycles were first made in the United States, 1878.

Rutherford B. Hayes was President, 1877-1881.

1879 FRANK STARTED HIS FIRST STORE AT UTICA, NEW YORK, THEN ONE AT LANCASTER, PENN-SYLVANIA.

Thomas Edison invented the electric light bulb, 1879.

The first electric street railway in the United States was operated in Baltimore, 1885.

Henry Ford built his first automobile in Detroit, 1896.

Wilbur and Orville Wright flew the first heavier-than-air aircraft, 1903.

1913 F. W. WOOLWORTH DEDICATED THE WOOL-WORTH BUILDING, IN NEW YORK CITY, APRIL 24.

The Panama Canal was completed and opened to world traffic, 1914.

World War I was fought, 1914-1918.

The United States entered World War I, 1917.

1919    F. W. WOOLWORTH DIED AT GLEN COVE, LONG
        ISLAND, NEW YORK, APRIL 9.

There were forty-eight states in the Union.

Woodrow Wilson was President.

The population of the country was about
104,335,000.

## DO YOU REMEMBER?

1. Why did the Woolworth family move to Great
   Bend when Frankie was six years old?

2. Why did Frankie like to visit McNeil's General
   Store?

3. Who was Miss Pennington and why did she come
   to the Woolworth home?

4. Where did schoolteachers usually live while they
   taught school?

5. What song did Frankie and his classmates learn
   to sing at school?

6. Why was Frankie especially interested in Napoleon Bonaparte?

7. Who was Joseph Bonaparte and why was his
   house called a cup-and-saucer house?

195

8. What different kinds of work did Frankie consider before he left the farm?

9. How did he manage to go to Commercial College for a few weeks?

10. How did he get his first offer to work in a store?

11. What kind of job did he get with Augsbury and Moore in Watertown?

12. What problems did he have during the next few years?

13. How did he get an opportunity to manage a five-cent department store?

14. How did Frank W. Woolworth organize his first store and why did it fail?

15. How did he manage to start another store in Lancaster, Pennsylvania?

16. What noted building did he erect in New York that came to be known as the Tower of Nickels and Dimes?

## IT'S FUN TO LOOK UP THESE THINGS

1. What is the meaning of the expression "Let the old cat die"? What is the meaning of the expression "Waste not, want not"?

2. Who built the cup-and-saucer house near Cape Vincent Village in New York, and how was the house used?

3. What kind of code do merchants often place on price tags in stores?

4. What is a calliope and how were calliopes once used in circuses?

5. Who are Pennsylvania Dutch, and how did they come to be called this name?

## INTERESTING THINGS YOU CAN DO

1. Visit an old-fashioned general store and describe it to the class.

2. Collect pictures of old stores and prepare a display on the bulletin board.

3. Draw a map showing where Frank Woolworth grew up and where he founded his first stores.

4. Visit a modern ten-cent store and compare it with the stores which Frank Woolworth first founded.

5. Read about Frank Woolworth's brother, Charles S. Woolworth, and explain how he helped to found the F. W. Woolworth Company.

## OTHER BOOKS YOU MAY ENJOY READING

*Andrew Carnegie and the Age of Steel*, Katherine B. Shippen. Trade Edition, Random House. School Edition, Hale.

*A. P. Giannini: Boy of San Francisco*, Marie Hammontree. Trade and School Editions, Bobbs-Merrill.

*John Wanamaker: Boy Merchant*, Olive W. Burt. Trade and School Editions, Bobbs-Merrill.

*Nickels and Dimes: the Story of F. W. Woolworth*, Nina Brown Baker. Harcourt.

*U. S. Grant*, Jeannette Covert Nolan. Grosset and Dunlap.

## INTERESTING WORDS IN THIS BOOK

**aisle** (īl) : passage between counters in a store

**au revoir** (ō rẽ vwär′) : French word, meaning good-by

**bandanna** (băn dăn′à) : large, figured handkerchief, usually red or blue

**barracks** (băr′ăks) : building for lodging soldiers

**break bread** (brāk′ brĕd′) : to eat food

**blizzard** (blĭz'ẽrd) : blinding snowstorm, accompanied by strong wind

**butterball** (bŭt'ẽr bôl') : slang for fat person

**byway** (bī'wā') : side road

**calico** (kăl'ĭ kō) : cheap cotton cloth with a figured pattern

**camp meeting** (kămp' mēt'ĭng) : religious services held in a tent or woods

**cathedral** (kȧ thē'drăl) : large church

**chickadee** (chĭk'ȧ dē) : small bird with black, white, and gray feathers

**dipper** (dĭp'ẽr) : cup with long handle

**disappear** (dĭs ă pēr') : go out of sight

**first-class** (fûrst'klȧs') : best, superior

**grindstone** (grīnd'stōn') : round, revolving stone, used to sharpen tools

**gumdrop** (gŭm'drŏp') : candy made of gelatin

**introduction** (ĭn trȯ dŭk'shŭn) : first part of a piece of music

**jawbreaker** (jô'brāk'ẽr) : hard candy balls

**licorice** (lĭk'ȯ rĭs) : candy flavored with sweet, black extract from the licorice plant

**oilcloth** (oil'klôth') : cloth coated with paint or oil to make it waterproof

**pass inspection** (păs ĭn spĕk'shŭn) : be examined for acceptance

**pleadingly** (plēd'ĭng lĭ) : in a begging manner

**pneumonia** (nu̇ mō'nĭ a̍) : disease of the lungs

**proficient** (prȯ fĭsh'ĕnt) : skilled

**raccoon** (ră kōōn') : small, grayish animal with a bushy, ringed tail, that moves about mostly at night

**rascal** (răs'kăl) : bad, dishonest person

**relax** (rė̍ lăks') : loosen

**skimp** (skĭmp) : to be saving

**spearmint** (spēr'mĭnt') : common, fragrant mint used for flavoring

**splendor** (splĕn'dēr) : brightness, brilliance

**spunk** (spŭngk) : spirit, courage

**stovepipe hat** (stōv'pīp hăt') : tall silk hat

**tomfoolery** (tŏm fōōl'ēr ĭ) : nonsense

**tootle** (tōō't'l) : toot gently and continuously on a flute

**whinny** (hwĭn'ĭ) : low, continuous neigh of a horse